The Long Goodbye
A Caregiver's Tale

by John W. Wilson

For more information, address:

PO Box 356 Johnson City, TX 78636

ISBN: 978-0-9710427-6-6

Gatewood

www.GatewoodPress.com

Dedication:

To Pharaby Wilson for a life of love.

To my children, Gabriel, Travis, and Brianne. Rocks to lean on one and all.

Foreword

I'm a caregiver. The patient is my wife. She has frontotemporal dementia, or FTD. What's captured here, in this book, are my thoughts and reactions over time as I came to terms with her disease. These mini-essays represent a curated selection of writings I've been publishing on social media since 2014. In the beginning, they were simply observations about the natural world of the Texas Hill Country. Gradually, however, my wife's disease came to occupy center stage; as it did, the essays became the public face of our life.

Each essay has a title and the date it was published. The latter is there to help the reader see the flow of events and feel the mounting and inexorable advance of the disease. This book contains very little about doctors and diagnoses. Rather, it describes how I, as the caregiver, responded to events, and how they drove my thought processes going forward. Armoring up, if you will, to face an uncertain future.

As the chronicle progresses, ordinary days, designed to provide a glimpse of our ordinary life, will be followed by days that became anything but. Unlike a novel, there are no surprise plot twists, no uplifting last-minute rescue. It's simply a plodding journey through something hundreds of families face on a daily basis when an apparently well-organized universe starts falling apart.

As I wrote, some of my friends began suggesting I share these essays with a wider audience. After all, caregiving is hardly confined to people affected by dementia; the struggle with loss is universal and covers a multitude of diseases and afflictions. So, I began to think my friends might be onto something, and here we are. If I can help even one person by sharing my experiences within the pages of this book, that's a good thing.

CONTENTS

Part 1: Being in Denial

W e had a normal life, my wife and me. We raised three children. Held jobs. Paid bills. Fought. Made up. Worked together as a team. Camped. Drank wine at the beach. Took trips. We met in 1969. Married in 1970. Lived in Pasadena and Alvin, Texas, eventually ending up in my ancestral hometown, Johnson City, in the Texas Hill Country in 2009. As time went on, we had the normal aches and pains. A few surgeries, trips to the doctor, mostly for things you'd expect from humans as they grow old.

Somewhere along the way, however, she began to notice she was having trouble finding words. It was one of the things she talked about with her doctor and sometimes with me, but I don't remember a specific first time I heard about it. Nothing that really rings a bell as being "the day" in which we learned our world was about to end. Eventually, when the doctor's visits led to neurologists and the conversations became increasingly serious, I started attending the sessions. At that point, the specter of Alzheimer's reared its head. But nothing was definitive. It seemed to be all guesswork. Still, we fought it, because neither one of us wanted to admit what might be at hand. She was up for anything that stretched her mental acuity. Puzzles, games, knitting, working on the computer. She immersed herself in her Daughters of the American Revolution (DAR) meetings and genealogy research. She could recite her lineage from memory going back generations.

As her illness progressed, we kept looking for answers, hoping against hope there was something that could be done that would reverse her decline. We worked our way through five neurologists, which is no knock on their skills. They were probably all telling us the same thing, just in slightly different terms. None of this made its way into my public writings, however, because when you're hoping to dodge a bullet there's no real point in talking about one that might be coming toward you.

The Day the Hummingbird Came

Tuesday, March 24, 2015

Yesterday morning we were sitting in the front room, drinking coffee, and watching the pasture. The birds were moving in and out of the hackberry. The early morning sun was still low in the sky. And off in the distance you could see the cattle grazing. There was little wind and the whirly-gig that our friends gave us this year after a visit to the California redwoods was hanging still in the morning air on the hook where we usually put the hummingbird feeder.

My wife casually wondered out loud, "When are the hummingbirds due back?" Just as I was about to answer that I didn't know, a hummingbird flew up, on cue, and hovered at the whirly-gig where normally he would have found nectar. That seemed a providential answer, so we moved the whirly-gig to a new location just down the porch, whipped up a batch of nectar, and put it out. That afternoon our early morning visitor came back and began feeding. Before the summer is out we'll be covered up in hummingbirds.

It will be interesting to see how the mockingbirds react to the crowds now that they have their own nest close by. So far, they seem ill-disposed to let any bird land anywhere close to their nest in the rosemary. Intruders are swiftly shooed off. Of course, the hummingbirds may be too small to cause the mockingbirds much concern. We'll see. Whatever happens, it's shaping up to be a good bird year in our little patch of the Hill Country, and life off the back porch will be bustling.

A Visit with the Kids

Friday, May 8, 2015

Stopped by the home of our oldest son yesterday on the way home from Houston. His wife cooked us dinner. Our granddaughter set the table, with my place beside hers. We served ourselves at the island, but all sat at the table together. For dessert we had a chocolate pudding that our granddaughter prepared. It was delightful, as was the entire meal.

When our own kids were young we always had sit-down dinners with no television. Everyone had their place. We conversed. We discovered things. Yesterday we did the same. It turns out that the grandson got to try a pair of the soon-to-be-released Oculus Rift Virtual Reality glasses, courtesy of a teacher and her engineer husband who was a beta-tester. It was a nice moment. The granddaughter professed her love for seafood, and tried to cajole me out of mine. I demurred.

As far as I'm concerned food has two purposes. One is sustenance. We have to eat. The other is to share with family and friends. I find it invigorating to sit at a table surrounded by people I love and like sharing a meal. The family meal of yesterday was that sort of event. A dinner of connections and memory, a foundation for the future. It was as nice a gift as a man could get. It made the long drive home easy.

Happy Birthday to You

Saturday, May 9, 2015

Yesterday was my wife's birthday. We met when she was 18, and I was 22. We married a year later. We're older than that now. Two of our three children are here to help celebrate the birthday and also Mother's Day on Sunday. There are presents, but their presence is more than enough. The joyful noise is back in the house. People, dogs, chatter. Tonight some friends are hosting a party. We'll make the hour-or-so drive to Austin, share memories, and get ready for another circle around the sun.

I enjoy birthdays. A celebration of the beginning of life and a marking of the journey. It is interesting as the numbers mount to realize the traveled road is longer than the one still to come but dwelling on it offers little value. It's best to simply continue the journey, take in the sights, and have a little fun.

Mother's Day is a slightly different story. My own mother passed away when I was 21, and she was 49. It was an abrupt end. There's a lot she missed. My wife, the kids, the grandkids. There was a lot they missed, too. Her. We have plenty of pictures and they know what she looked like, but the person is a mystery. There's little I can say that makes her more real to them. I try but it's hard and I don't dwell on it. I think the best bet is to celebrate with the living and offer gratitude for the mothers we have, the mothers we've known, and the mothers still to come.

The Newest Member of the Family

Thursday, June 4, 2015

There's a new dog in the house. Timmy. He's small, seven months old; a black and white Chihuahua terrier mix. He's a perky pet in a good way. Boundless energy and boundless love. He's finding his way around the rules of the house and getting acclimated to using outdoor facilities. His percentage is rising, which is a good trend. One hundred percent may be unobtainable, but ninety would be better.

It seems as though he prefers to sniff strangers in the house rather than barking them up. Perhaps he intuitively understands that his size puts him at a disadvantage and it might be wiser to keep quiet until he can accurately assess the new presence in the house. He likes laps, but seems to prefer the blanket on the couch for naps. We keep his kennel in the utility room and he retires there at night and when we're out of the house for extended periods during the day. Unlike previous pets there's no frantic scratching or complaining. He knocks around, snacks, and goes to bed. That's good.

If we leave him out of the kennel when we're gone, our clothes, shoes and socks mysteriously gather in the center of various rooms for some sort of mystical dog party. He invites my wife's crochet materials on occasion, which produces a high level of human wailing. There's no evidence of chewing, just gathering. He'll probably never provide a satisfactory explanation. One offshoot is that we're doing a much better job of keeping things picked up and closet doors closed. So the house looks tidy. We're hoping he grows out of it, but while we wait it's easier to change our ways than his.

In the Footsteps

Wednesday, July 29, 2015

My mother was a registered nurse, my father a retired Navy hospital corpsman. I followed in his footsteps for a time. I am comfortable in the halls of hospitals and the rooms of nursing homes. I know the sights and sounds. I trust doctors and their staffs. I know the questions to ask and the signs to observe. When any of our family goes to a hospital I expect a good outcome. The technology and knowledge of the medical establishment is superb.

I also believe in the power of prayer. In the early 1980s I had a hernia repaired. I asked people to think of me and offer up a prayer. After the surgery, as I was lying in recovery, I swore I could feel the presence of hands on my back supporting and comforting me. I have no doubt, that in the interconnected web of the universe, all those people directing thoughts in my direction brought me comfort. The prayers came home.

I say this because in the morning my wife will have a knee replaced. A team of talented people will work to make her life better. I trust them and expect good things, in part because they are skilled, but also because I know our friends and family will be praying for her. She won't go into the operating room alone, nor will she have to bear the recovery by herself. She will be carried along by love and prayers. Both will flow, hands will support her, and the pain will abate. She may well be starting on an arduous journey when it's time to rehab her knee, but it will be made better by the company of friends who, if need be, will carry her across the finish line.

A View from the Downside

Saturday, August 8, 2015

This has been the summer of medicine. First, Bell's Palsy drooped my face and eye. Then my bride had a total knee replacement. The Palsy has abated, and my wife is now walking with a cane one week after they machined her knee and installed new parts. Dealing with these frailties has drained us both, but family and friends have rallied round and it appears we will prevail. There is a tendency in times like these to think, *woe is me*, and hop on board the pity train. But this is the point when it pays to look up because there is trouble all around.

My friend since high school is battling prostate cancer and it's proving a hard fight. But he's climbed almost all the highest peaks in these fifty States, and when I talk to him I realize he views his trouble as simply one more mountain to climb. I have no doubt he'll summit, soak in the view from the top, and set off on more adventures. Closer to home, the daughter of one of our neighbors rolled her car last summer right before her senior year and is now quadriplegic. She graduated high school though, and her wonderfully resilient family appears to have embarked on this new journey with courage and faith.

I could continue the litany of surgeries and death but I think the point is made. Life is hills and valleys, and guaranteed to end poorly. There is suffering all around, and a lot of folks are walking a harder road. So, I try to endure, take pleasures where I find them, and enjoy the simple acts of breathing and looking around. At the moment, I am going to stand on the front porch, watch the first light of day fall on the pasture, and feel the cool morning breeze blowing in from the south.

Lending a Helping Hand

Wednesday, August 26, 2015

On Sunday past I happened to stop in the living room and look out the windows toward the pasture. As I did, I noticed a pair of scissortails sitting close together on the fence. Suddenly one of them fluttered up off the wire and dropped down to the vines growing beneath them.

It picked a berry of some sort. It fluttered back up to the top wire, berry in beak. This is where the story diverges from expectations. It turned to the bird sitting next to it and offered it the berry. Its companion took the berry and ate it. The two birds then sat in silence looking out at the pasture. A minute or so later the routine was repeated. I can only guess at the birds' relationship. I assume adult and juvenile. I am not well enough versed in the plumages of scissortails to know with any certainty.

What struck me about the transaction was its gentleness. I've seen feeding behavior in a nest. The young birds are shrill and insistent. This was simply two companions sitting together with one offering the other food. Here, try this, it tastes good. A husband and wife. A mother and child. Two lovers. I felt as though I had glimpsed an intimate moment, a piece of their lives seldom seen, an action that defined or cemented a relationship. They flew off soon after without warning or apparent provocation. Birds being birds. As I watched them go, I was left to wonder what, if anything, it meant. I do know it made me feel good.

Observations beneath a Tree

Monday, September 7, 2015

On Friday past, as evening approached, I found myself sitting beneath a big oak looking up through its branches and leaves at the sky. The huge trunk with thick limbs was supporting an array of increasingly smaller limbs all designed to bear tiny, fragile leaves and hold them up to the sun. Some were successful at finding space and light, while others had lost their way and were trapped in dark spaces. One limb was bent down at a right angle for no apparent reason and yet had continued to send smaller branches skyward. Its girth was testimony to the span of its efforts. My tree viewing ended as the sun set. The leaves and the dark sky merged into black.

As I walked out from under the tree's canopy and into the anonymous night, I thought of my uncle who had passed away that morning. He was the last survivor of three Wilson boys of which my father was the oldest. He left behind two daughters and a group of grandchildren and great-grandchildren. He, too, liked to sit in the shade of trees, in particular the ones that graced his front yard in San Antonio.

There's more to his story, of course: a B-17 waist gunner; career Air Force; second career Postal Service; four children; and a good wife who passed before him. He was a man who loved travel and who loved his family. He did his best to care for those he brought into the world and those they brought in as well. By now, I am familiar with the rhythms of death, the passing, the remembrance, and the services, followed by the emptiness that only partially disappears. I am ready to endure it once again. He will be missed by all. I imagine his trees will miss him as well.

Survival Skill

Tuesday, September 8, 2015

When I get down in the dumps I like to climb out by putting myself to work. Get sweaty. Fix things. Move stuff around. I've been dumpy the last several days, so on Monday I got up and got after it. Our old fence had been coming apart at the seams so I pulled it back together. The work involved drills, ratchets and lag bolts. It's not perfect but it will hold a while longer. I broke a ceramic sun hanging on the fence. That will need to be replaced. Tried fixing it. Impossible.

Also, I pulled out the hose and the broom and cleaned the swallow poop off the back porch. Moved all the chairs out into the yard and washed them as well. Cleaned up about 50 peach pits the rock squirrels had left behind the chest where we keep the chair cushions. Should have done that a while ago. Normally my bride would have reminded me, but I think her knee issues have adversely affected her focus. At any rate, we're ready for fall and for back porch visitors. Dust will still accumulate, but that's easily handled.

I'm a procrastinator by nature so the dumps don't do me any favors. I tend to fret as well. If anyone wanted to start a business making mountains out of mole hills, I'd be a great addition to the staff. I can create elaborate scenarios in my head all based on my imagination and worry myself into a nearly catatonic state. That's why work is so good. The sweat, the focus, the effort beat back the demons and cut off their running room. Unfed, they skulk off. All that's left to do is clean up and start moving forward once again, reminding myself that life is a journey best lived one day at a time.

Services

Friday, September 11, 2015

Buried my uncle yesterday. Got washed by the rain on the way home. I hope it's the start of our wet winter. My uncle's service was graveside in a country cemetery just outside Richards, Texas. Laid him beside his wife and youngest daughter. They played taps, saluted with rifles, and gave his flag to his daughter on behalf of a grateful nation. We melted in the heat and humidity and the loss.

Afterwards we met in the old church building at the cemetery to eat food prepared by strangers. The air conditioning was welcome. As we ate, we renewed family bonds, talked to the youngsters, and made promises that we needed to get together again sooner rather than later. As a family, we're actually pretty good about that. We know cousins, children of cousins and their children, too. We tend to see one another fairly often just to socialize.

It was odd, during the service, to look around and realize I'd known the man longer than almost everyone standing there mourning his loss. Of course, I've understood for some time I was aging. That realization is hard to avoid. It's just that now a lot of the people in my old pictures are dead. Well. Life goes on and I'm still in the business of making memories. Maybe I'll pester my grandkids next week.

A Weekend of Normal

Saturday, September 12, 2015

C old front is here. Temperature this morning is 71 degrees. Should get down to the low 60s tonight. It's about time. It was a norther for sure, just not blue. We've gotten rain all around the last several days, but none at the homestead. I hope we get our turn. I imagine we will. It only seems fair. I think this is where folks that live in the Northern climes start laughing at us, or maybe with us. Who knows?

I do know we made some friends at our church back in the 1980s who'd migrated here from Buffalo, New York. They loved their city, but they liked wearing shorts in January. They're still here in Texas, and their children are here and now their grandchildren. I need to ask them if they explain about lake-effect snow whenever the kids complain about the heat. You know, the when-I-was-a-kid speech.

This is shaping up to be a do-nothing weekend and for that I am glad. We were supposed to be in the mountains of New Mexico, but events conspired against us. Maybe next year. Today I'll probably watch a little football or golf and certainly take a nap. My wife made a pot of chicken gumbo last night in anticipation of the weather change. It's a meal that ages well. It's in a class with pinto beans or meatloaf. I'll have the gumbo for lunch and maybe even dinner. I may even get up from my chair once in a while.

Holiday Work

Saturday, October 3, 2015

Brisk. The temperature is in the 50s this morning. Wispy clouds are turning pink with the early sun against a light blue sky. The dry grass is gold. A deer is running in the open at the edge of the far tree line. Nary a breath of air. All is still.

Yesterday my neighbor installed the old metal windsock that used to guide pilots into the Waller Airport. You can find it on some old maps. The grass landing strip was in the pasture behind my house. He found the sock in his basement. Another neighbor repaired it, banged out some dents and did a bit of minor welding. It's always good to have a neighbor who welds. The pipe where the windsock originally stood is right by my back fence, but it wouldn't have been visible from his house. So, he moved it. Fine with me, now we can both watch it turn in the wind.

My wife is crocheting orange doilies for Halloween. Boat load of work for a one-day holiday, but I suspect they'll go out around the house a few days before, probably a week. We have a doily my grandmother crocheted, framed and hanging on the wall. If the kids decide to frame all the doilies their mother has produced, they won't have to bother painting the walls. I suspect, however, as with most artifacts of a person's life the little doilies will simply drift off into oblivion, one at a time, to be pondered over in a thrift shop. Now why would we want an orange doily? And no one will think of Halloween.

Getting the Call

Saturday, November 14, 2015

The call you never want to get. Hello, this is (nice sounding young lady). I'm a social worker with (name of local hospital). Your (loved one's name) was involved in a car accident and is here with us. Two things happen in short order: establishing status of the kin, and calculating the length of time it will take to arrive on location. Calming the beating heart is an important part of the drill.

Got this very call Wednesday evening around five. The kin in question was my wife. Arrived to find her bruised, a tiny bit broken, and crying. A day and a half of various therapies and observations and we were released to go home yesterday. Made the trip with only a tiny bit of pain and got settled into the favorite chair for recovery. Daughter and oldest son arrived to join the son already on location and complete the ensemble. The music of laughing children once again played in the room.

As burdens go, I suspect this will be a light one. Progress is noticeable. It does call to mind, however, those who carry heavier loads. My friend who just lost a young cousin to a car accident. Last year, when another friend's daughter became a paraplegic. I think the key to surviving this sort of sorrow and heartbreak is the understanding that for every stone you're asked to carry someone else has most likely gathered two. It also helps when friends and family surge in and gather round to offer comfort with loving arms and words of kind support.

A Day Like Any Other

Thursday, November 26, 2015

Thanksgiving has always been a betwixt and between holiday for me. There are no great Thanksgiving memories. As a child, traveling the country, there was the standard fare of Pilgrims and Indians, corn and turkeys in the schools, but I'm unable to recall my parents celebrating the holiday with any great relish or fanfare. It came, we ate, we got ready for Advent.

The holiday became more of a thing as I got older. Marriage pulled me into a family where food was an essential part of any gathering. If you came for even a short visit the big pots were pulled out, the rice was cooked, and gumbo filled the bowls. Thanksgiving was a holiday made for eating. Since we lived just down the road from my mother-in-law and she loved to cook, we often found ourselves at her table. After she passed my wife picked up the gauntlet and we feasted at our house as younger brothers and sisters gathered. Eventually, however, they began building their own families and moved off as did our children. The impetus for a feast faded.

Nowadays we go with the flow. Usually eating out, dining in where invited, relaxing and taking things as they come. Maybe it's part of aging. I'm happy to be where I am with a great family, good friends, and plenty of blessings. There are burdens to be sure but all of the above help me bear them and while I realize setting aside one day to say thanks is a fine idea, doing it every day is probably a better choice.

Grim Reminders

Saturday, December 19, 2015

O n random occasions I find myself facing the anxiety of losing it all and ending up on the street, hungry and seeking shelter. Most likely it's a buried hunter-gatherer gene designed to keep me hunting and gathering. When your next meal was on the hoof or vine, it paid to focus. Complacency was the enemy. Relaxing and believing you had it made was a recipe for disaster. If the game walked off and you failed to notice, that was bad.

The feeling came to me this morning as I stood on the back porch and felt the chill of the returning cold in the predawn darkness. In the days previous a friend of mine had lost his job, and another discovered he had cancer. It seemed the world was busy proving its hardness and how it dealt with life. The cold reminded me.

I stood for a second to let the lesson sink in. Behind me, in the house, my wife prepared breakfast while Bing Crosby sang Christmas songs, and my son slept soundly in the guest room. I turned and walked up the stairs to my office and left the dark and cold to their own devices. Over the years, I've come to understand several things. Bridges are best crossed when you come to them. Hard times require a steely-eyed pragmatism. Loss is inevitable. Friends in need or sick deserve support, a kind word and any helping hand that can be proffered.

The River Trip

Wednesday, February 17, 2016

The other day I was standing under the big oaks by our water feature watching the water run over the rocks and listening to it fall into the tank below. The new electric pump was a splendid addition and now that the water runs and falls consistently, it has a newfound clarity. The sound of the pure falling water reminded me of the shallow Texas rivers I've frequented with waters that run up and over and beneath all sort of rocks as they make their way along. The sound is hypnotic, the water clear, and I've listened to it and watched it for hours. I was glad I had a little taste of it beneath my trees.

The birds and squirrels like our clear moving water as well. The other day I watched a flock of starlings socialize at the tank, drinking and bathing and having a good ole time. It was a big flock and they came in shifts. Listening to them I fully expected to see little coolers of beer. The squirrels usually come alone, standing on the edge, dipping down to drink and quench their thirst. I've never seen them bathe. Even our little dog, Timmy, enjoys a drink of the clear cold water.

We missed our annual trip to the river last year. My wife's bad knee made the trip untenable. The knee got replaced over the summer, however, so the trip will probably be made once again. Getting down to the river is a bit of a trick, but her new-found mobility will see her through. We'll just go slow. When we get there we'll put our chairs in the free-flowing waters, sit in the shade and visit with our friends. Unlike the starlings, we'll have a cooler full of beer.

Dirt Work

Tuesday, March 22, 2016

Well, the killer frost came to visit. The tomato plants are saved. Lots of other young leaves, however, bit the dust. The exposed crape myrtles lost some, and the morning glory did as well. A frostbit leaf is an evil dark green and it loses it shape, a victim of the ice within that breaks down the plant's cells. Everything beneath the canopy of the big trees fared well. Thankfully, it was simply a frost rather than a hard freeze. The plants themselves should recover as the warmth and longer days continue.

We finished weeding the rest of the back flower bed yesterday morning. It was a combined effort. My wife rode her small garden stool while I wielded the pitchfork from my knees, slamming it into the ground, digging deep to get the thistle and hedge parsley, pulling them clear and knocking the dirt loose from the roots. For the moment the bed looks well-manicured, and a good home for the laurels and fruit trees. Next weekend we attack the beds beneath the big oaks. I've been there once, but they regressed. I shall return.

I always feel energized during this season of growing things. Working in the dirt is cathartic, particularly when it is dirt I've worked for many seasons and I find it moist and rich with odors as the mulch and leaves decay, and work their way into the soil. It says: *I'm healthy.* The nicely groomed flower beds speak to a sense of order and clean canvas where beauty is encouraged and given space to flourish. There is certainly beauty in wildness but every once in a while, the gentle things need help to avoid being crushed by the rough edges of the thistles and their kin. They need gardens. They need space. They need peace. They need love.

No Fools Here

Friday, April 1, 2016

My wife and I went to New Braunfels yesterday to visit a dentist. On the way home we stopped at a café we frequent for a small bite of lunch. Shared a sandwich as we tend to do and sat and watched the people. The sounds of conversation bubbled around the room, low and muted. Made me think of times I'd spent on the banks of creeks and rivers.

I think this is why people enjoy eating out. The sounds of other people. The flock, the herd, the community. You sit there with your spouse, your friend, your companion, your co-worker, your thoughts, and enjoy the food, their company, the ideas, and hear other people doing the same. There's a sense that this is right and good.

We finished our meal and left. As we walked to our car, I saw an acquaintance in the distance entering the post office. She was talking to a worker standing outside and she was moving with a purpose. There was no real chance to say hello. We passed. She went in to get her mail, and we drove home for a nap. The food, the voices, the faces, were in my thoughts as I dozed off. It was a nice way to end the morning.

A New Family Member Arrives

Monday, June 20, 2016

For Father's Day I got a Yeti mug and a son-in-law. The mug came from my oldest boy and his family. The son-in-law was courtesy of my daughter. The mug is great and really does keep drinks cold and won't sweat on the outside. The son-in-law is great, too. He's an Army guy who served in Afghanistan, is now in the Reserves, and works as an assistant principal. He just got a letter announcing his acceptance into the doctoral program for Education at the University of Houston.

Our daughter is very happy with this young man, as are we. He's from Maine and seems endowed with a very level head. A group of his friends flew in for the wedding as did his grandmother and mother. My brother, the ex-cowboy preacher, performed the wedding at the old firehouse in the Houston Heights. Afterwards, we repaired downstairs to eat, drink, and dance. It was a family affair with aunts and nieces and friends all pitching in to set up, take down, serve the food, and just generally keep the proceedings moving. On Saturday morning, I had a brief attack of I-need-to-take-charge before I realized everything was under control and I just had to be the father of the bride.

After that it was easy. She and I had a great walk down the aisle. We danced to Paul Simon's "Father Daughter." She cried; I cried. It was good. Later that evening I sang "You Never Even Called Me by My Name" with my son and his son and all of our friends which is a party tradition going back to the day after the song first came out. When all was said and done, the newlyweds walked off into the evening to a nearby Bed and Breakfast. The world turned and circled the sun as life moved forward, and my family grew by one.

The New Extended Family

Thursday, June 30, 2016

The big trip to the East Coast is in the books. Our new son-in-law went home to Maine to introduce his bride to friends and family, all lovely, gracious people. We went along for the ride. We got the chef's tour of his old stomping grounds from Scarborough, inland to Dexter where we ate a pot of steamed lobster and clams beside a lake and saw a loon. Most of the tour focused on the Coast, which was fine with us since my wife and I both have a proclivity for the sea and the shore. By all accounts there's still more to see and I'd really like to see it. There's nothing like a host who loves his land.

On our last day there, after the kids had departed for a true honeymoon, we drove into the Granite State and made our way north into New Hampshire's Ossipee Mountain Range, the remains of an ancient volcano. These are big mountains by Texas standards and were great fun to drive through. Eventually, we made our way to the top of one of them and looked down into the valleys below filled with lakes and forests.

We made the trip home without incident although it was long and involved a drive into our own Hill Country at the end of a hard day of air travel. Home and bed felt great. This morning the air is cool and our own little hills off across the pasture are bathed in sunlight, small reflections of their Eastern kin. As the day progresses, I'll find a way to step back into the routine of home life bolstered by some fine memories and ready to make some more when the opportunity arises.

Thoughts of the Moonlit Beach

Tuesday, July 19, 2016

T he moon is full this morning, hanging low on the horizon off to the southwest. To see it, I have to go to the end of the front porch and step out onto the apron of the carport. It feels close in its brightness, and I can see the shadows of the craters and mountains. It seems eons ago that the moon was a source of constant fascination as men and machines flew toward it and around it and ultimately, landed on it. Of all the things I've seen in my lifetime, that was the best.

Now, the moon hangs in the sky, forgotten, running through its endless cycle on autopilot, largely ignored by the populace. No one even writes a song to it these days. Perhaps by landing on it we killed its romance. Sad. When my wife and I first empty-nested, we made a ritual of going to the beach in Galveston on the night of the full moon with our reclining lawn chairs and a bottle of wine. The daytime beach goers would leave us to our own devices. The privacy was nice.

We're further inland now and the sea and the shore a bit further off. We may have to take a road trip. I'm feeling a bit melancholy for the old days, and an evening on the beach with some wine may be just the ticket to lift my spirits. Sometimes, just thinking about it is enough to do the trick. In the meantime, out my window, I can see the rosy glow of the morning sun as the earth makes a slow turn across the dancefloor of the heavens, spinning under the outstretched arms of it partner, the sun. It's a new day. It will be interesting to see what will come of it.

Thoughts of Yesterday

Wednesday, July 20, 2016

Two years ago, we installed an above ground pool. We needed it because water was recommended as an exercise medium for my wife's bad knees. It provided the needed relief. Last year when one of the knees was replaced the pool got little use, but the new knee was a great improvement. This year the pool is back in the rotation because it's a big body of water and it's cool in the evening and we've got it, so, what the heck.

I've joined in as well. I'm unsure as to why I eschewed the pool during its early tenure, but I did. Perhaps it was my travel schedule which has abated this year. At any rate, most early evenings will find us floating about in the cool, clear water talking over the day's events, planning for the next day or sometimes saying nothing at all, just being together. Yesterday, I found myself floating on my back, holding my wife's hand, staring up at the sky watching the clouds slide by. They drifted and turned across the heavens, folding in on themselves, stretching into wispy vapors, and on occasion darkening and looking like rain.

Yesterday's visitors were coming from the south, vapors from the Gulf. As we floated, and I watched, it reminded me of a time when we first dated. We would go to a secluded spot by the bay in a close-by industrial area where the pasture dropped off as a cliff down into the water. But just over the edge there was another flat piece that had broken off from its pasture and slid down, large enough for two, where we could spread a blanket and watch the water and the sky in private. It was a pleasant way for two kids with no money to spend an afternoon and start a life together.

Flowers of Love

Thursday, October 6, 2016

It's aster time again. The blooms are popping out all over the large array of plants we now have growing beneath the side-garden's lacey oak. The Gulf muhly that normally joins the show won't be appearing this year; the grass is in decline and needs replacing. The asters, meanwhile, are making up for the loss. Lovely to have them, and I think well of the gentle person who gave us the original plant every time they bloom.

We have other plants that are memorials to loved ones. Bulbs from my mother-in-law's garden, and from my wife's aunt in Louisiana. They show up each spring along with the spiderworts my great-grandmother used to cultivate by the house next to ours. All of which bloom and propagate and make more of themselves to help keep the memories alive. In addition, I have plants I've retrieved from various wild locations. My single scarlet sage, dug from a fence line years ago, has turned into a veritable forest of plants, and my blackfoot daisies, dug from a friend's ranch, live in every corner of the garden.

I like my plants. They only want a place to live and a bit of water to drink. Then, they go on about their business and reward you with a fistful of blooms, a bright spot of color in an otherwise dull day, or a celebratory burst to revel in the sunshine. Of course, there are those that stick you if you grab them too hard, or give you a blister if rubbed the wrong way, but they, too, have their place in the garden. It's the joys and challenges that bring a garden to life and reward you well if you find the skills to deal with them.

A Toast

Monday, October 10, 2016

It feels like a good day to count blessings. On Friday we were invited to join a group of friends for dinner and music. On Saturday, a friend-of-a-friend came over to talk to me about some work that needs doing. The conversation was productive. Later in the afternoon another friend came over to watch football. Our team lost for the first time this year, but there's always tomorrow, or next Saturday to be more precise. Then yesterday we got a couple of texts from an out-of-state friend who wanted to know if we'd be around Tuesday for lunch, an unexpected pleasure.

Last week I got bubbly calls from my daughter and from my oldest son about their work. I had a great lunch with a musician friend, followed by a trip to Austin with my wife to see him and the band in which he plays, which is comprised of an entire group of friends. At our table we were surrounded by another group of friends, fans of the band, and it made for a great evening and all I had to drink was a soda.

On the family side, both of my brothers live close by, and we talk, while I have a great group of cousins living all across the state from Dallas south to San Antonio. My wife's family is likewise close at hand and in the picture. The dog sits on my lap and the cat rubs on my leg. I still can't install the latest Windows 10 anniversary update on my computer, but it will happen one day if I have patience. On a closing note, I shot an 89 the last time I played golf and I did it by making a 15-foot putt on the final hole. Here's to an old man's friends and family. I raise a glass to you all.

Home Again from a Sad Trip

Friday, October 21, 2016

J ust back from Louisiana where we celebrated the life of a departed son. He was the only child of my wife's cousin and her husband, done in by cancer. He left too soon, only in his late fifties, with two boys of his own and three grandchildren. His parents weep as only parents who've lost a child can do.

I first met him when he was eleven and my wife took me, the new boy in the family, to meet her kin. I watched the young man grow up, living life with gusto. He wanted his time on the water, in the marshes, and running with his friends. He farmed rice, worked in the mills, got married, got divorced, stayed in touch with his wife. She was there, crying at his departure. She'd held his hand for his last breath. I always admired his hell-bent-for-leather approach and total lack of fear. It's fair to say he lived a full life.

Now comes the hard part, for the family, as they have to deal with the new hole in their lives. Even though we all know, as a matter of course, that death will come, there's nothing that makes it easy. Right now is the time for tears. But even as we gathered to eat and grieve there was laughter at the bright memories and big smile. Eventually, that is what will save us. That, and the reflection of his face in the eyes of his sons and grandchildren, because we know, in them, his faint heart still beats.

Another Dip

Saturday, October 29, 2016

There's a fog out in the pasture. It's sitting down in the lowland by the creek, which is only a creek when it rains. I suppose it once flowed, but those days are past. The rising population and shrinking water table have seen to that. Still, the scene is tranquil and quiet which is a nice balm for the soul. I can use a balmy day or two.

We had originally planned on being in Houston today, but called off the trip. I think I've reached my quota of road time on Highway 290, Highway 71 and Interstate 10. At least for a while. I need to shrink back into myself for a bit and just sit. Well, not actually sit. There's work around the house that needs doing, even if it's only important to me. I mowed the wildflower garden yesterday, trimmed up the edges around the border and took a stab at cleaning the path. It seemed productive and that may be all that counts.

It seems I've slipped into a funk of sorts, and usually the best way out is to circle the wagons and try to take control of my immediate surroundings. So, watch out weeds and bushes, here I come. The leggy Turks caps will be trimmed, and there's a grapevine that needs removing. I'll also mow our new little lawn with the manual push mower, which is an oddly satisfying chore. I'd clean the workroom, but I'm currently sharing it with my son's electronic equipment and there's not much space to move. It can wait. I may also find some time to just sit in the sun. I think that would be most helpful. And maybe I'll call a friend to just talk.

Holiday Prep

Saturday, November 26, 2016

The air this morning is still and chill with hardly a breeze. The pasture is lit beneath the trees by the first rays of the sun. No deer to be seen, or cattle. A few birdcalls sound off in the distance. Clouds are building to the north and west. Rain may come tomorrow, but for now, nothing. It is simply an uneventful beginning of a winter morning.

They lit the Courthouse last night and turned on the lights in the Pedernales Electric Coop (we call it PEC) courtyard. All the big oaks are lit to a fare-thee-well. We watched the fireworks from our driveway. They were easy to see and fun to watch until the cold chased us back indoors. We could hear the dance music from the square into the evening. We'll take our own private viewing later this week when the crowds have thinned and parking and navigation are easier.

I'll probably start hanging our own lights today and tomorrow. I have plenty of time, now that I'm retired and no longer making the weekly grind back and forth to Houston. Takes off all the pressure. Of course, my procrastination gene is still pretty strong and the extra time at home simply means I have more places to store the things I need to do. My bride may give me a friendly prod in the right direction. I could wait and see. Or, I could pretend I'm a grownup and just get it done. The eternal struggle.

31

Weird Weather

Monday, November 28, 2016

G ot up this morning, looked outside, and thought: blah. Another gray day. A few moments later my wife came out of the bedroom, looked outside, and said, "Oh, how beautiful." I think I'll go with that. Seems like a better approach. Besides, it's probably unfair to condemn an entire day because I may have gotten up on the wrong side of the bed and only saw the gray when I should have seen the blue.

I started the winter yard work yesterday. Trimmed up some of the over-reaching vines that had called it quits with the most recent freeze. The runners are still a healthy green when cut, but the leaves are mostly gone. Also, went along and pulled up errant grasses from the flower beds. They've had time to seed, but that will be next spring's problem. The Bermuda is starting to go dormant, but there are interesting mottled lines of dark green still remaining. I guess some things just don't want to go to sleep for the winter.

Speaking of winter, it's been an odd one so far. We're nearly to December with only one really good cold spell. The weather service thinks we'll be in for more of the same, sort of up and down, since the La Niña is stuck in neutral and hardly amounting to much. Accordingly, we may hit January and get covered up in snow, only to start wearing shorts in February. I suppose the best bet is to take things one day at a time and be happy with what we've got no matter how wet, warm, windy, wild, or frigid it may be. It's winter in Texas. Shorts and parkas at the ready.

Waiting on Santa

Saturday, December 24, 2016

Today's the day. And although my first thought is of teddy bears and picnics, what I really mean is Christmas Eve. A day of high anticipation, of evening vigils and midnight masses. In my youth it was the day we put up the Christmas tree. Even as the oldest son, however, I never got old enough to earn a night with my parents to put out presents. That's probably a good thing because in my mind I'll always be their child and Santa never comes until I go to sleep.

At our house, the son-in-law arrives today, and that will complete this year's family gathering. The daughter spent yesterday evening completing his new Christmas stocking with his name in gold threaded script. It now hangs from the chimney with care along with those crafted by my wife over the years. The oldest, with his kids, has obligations to his wife's family this year. We spread the season's joy with them last weekend. It was good and brightened considerably when the grandson opined that he wished he was coming to Johnson City. But that, too, is part of the season, learning the obligations and doing them with joy.

Tomorrow will bring the gathering around the tree. Coffee cups in hand, laughter in the room. Presents handed out. Hope springing eternal that the recipient will be pleased at the offering. Presents opened. Smiles. Thank you's. Then the paper will be gathered, the room cleaned, and the cooking begin. We'll share food and more laughter until it comes time for departures. Life will return, more or less, to normal, and our thoughts will turn to the New Year and what it may have to offer.

A Nod to Shakespeare

Saturday, December 31, 2016

Stayed up late. Woke up late. Missed today's curtain rise. The world was well lit and the other actors were on the stage when I arose. The wife was glad to see me because she needed the facilities, and the cats were all there when I walked out the door carrying their feeder. Then it occurred to me that perhaps my entrance was simply timed differently today. It's a small scene this morning. I went with it.

I've only seen the outlines of today's script. It seems promising. My school is playing basketball at noon, and later we'll hook up with friends and welcome in the New Year. Or at least try. As I get older, celebrating the clock tick that turns the page on a Gregorian calendar has seemed less and less important. I've surrendered to my body and its demands for sleep. Plus, the ravages of alcohol scheduled for tomorrow, if I give in tonight, is something I'd rather forego. I think I'll walk up to the edge and peer over rather than jump.

Some might call that wisdom. I think it's simply another name for fatigue and old age. It's akin to the feeling you get when the "need gas" light comes on and the speedometer tells you how many miles to empty. You start turning off things and slowing down to limp to the next station. Personally, I'd like my life trip to last a little longer, to tarry a bit on the stage. A number of new characters have entered and I'd like to get to know them better before I pass. We hung out with a lot of them last night. Everyone is full of laughter. In addition, they make loads of good music; of just the type I'd like to have played when I'm heading off the stage for the last time, when the time comes.

Comes the Cold

Thursday, January 5, 2017

On the ninth and tenth day of Christmas I took down our Christmas decorations. They're all safely boxed and labeled in the attic. The organization is designed to make it easier for next year. Of course, experience has taught me that the organization will somehow come apart in the intervening 360-plus days. Things will get moved, boxes pushed around, and memories tangled. By Christmas 2017 the labels will become less than precise, and I'll stare blankly at strings of lights and try to remember how they went up.

Maybe that's part of the fun. Putting up the lights, making the adjustments, creating something new out of something similar. Changing it up, but not too much. Sometimes we talk about going all in and making wholesale changes. For instance, we've talked about moving away from icicle lights hanging on the house. But that resolve usually fades because new lights cost money and these work just fine. Well, nearly fine. There is one blank spot where a few of the icicle lights are out. I've tried repairing it, but anyone who has tried to fix a string of Christmas lights knows the futility of that exercise. I leave it as a symbol of humility. A sign that no one is perfect.

Those who know me well, however, may challenge that by simply stating I'm just too lazy or cheap to fix it. I'm good with that. Maybe next year I could buy a new string so that all the lights come on. That's probably a bridge to cross at some point in the future, which fits perfectly with my tendency to procrastinate. I'll put them up and see how the spirit moves me. Usually the spirit reveals itself in the form of my wife who is less inclined to symbolic gestures than I am. She let it go this year, but may feel less inclined to do so next year. We'll see. Here's to the spirit.

Down Memory Lane

Monday, February 13, 2017

It was a road trip weekend, Friday to Sunday. On the first night we watched the grandson pitch four sterling innings to take the win. He even took a line drive off the foot, which only seemed to irritate him and make him harder to hit. On the next two days, the oldest son and I went to a card show where twelve members of Phi Slamma Jama, the University of Houston's legendary basketball team, were signing autographs. We had them sign media guides and programs, the detritus of my life as a fan of UH athletics.

One of the artifacts was a small poster handed out after Coach Guy V. Lewis won his 500th game against Arizona on November 26, 1982 as part of the Kettle Classic. My son's claim to fame was that the 501st win on November 28th in the finals against Lamar was the first basketball game he and his younger brother ever attended, as I duly noted in the program I saved from that night. It was a nice talking point and the players were interested to hear about it.

Overall, it was a pleasant walk down memory lane. Every player who signed was gracious and kind. They asked our names, shook hands, posed for pictures, and just generally appreciated the attention. They marveled at pictures of their younger selves, pointing out items of interest to wives and friends. Some even took pictures. When we wrapped it all up, my wife and I made the long drive home in the dark to be greeted by the younger son and the cats and the dogs. All were glad to see us, and our own big bed felt fine.

When the Sun Comes

Friday, March 24, 2017

D rove through town yesterday. Saw a blind man walking down the street, his cane sweeping the path before him. A little further on I saw a sighted man standing on a corner staring down at his smart phone. I wondered: if the blind man were to suddenly see, would he watch a phone, or look up at the world around him? Hard to tell. No matter where you look there's always something to miss.

The drive ended at my favorite book store. I had a nice visit with the smell of ink and paper. Bought a couple of books, drank a cup of coffee and ate a cookie. When I finished, I retrieved my wife from her DAR meeting and we went to get a bit of lunch before heading home. The wind was howling as we drove, kicking up big clouds of white dust from the construction sites lining Highway 290 west of Austin. It's being built and they're coming—who and what, exactly, remains to be seen.

There should be rain this morning as we continue our journey into spring. I hope it comes. I still have garden work to do, and it's always easier when the ground is moist and the little bits of dirt are held apart by water. The soil gives up its plants without much fuss. It will also help keep the cool in the air, which a good part of spring. Lately the sun has heated the afternoons to a summer quality, which is not at all appealing for this time of year. Although I guess that's why I have a porch. To sit in the shade when the hot sun comes.

The Narrow View

Monday, April 3, 2017

I like the digital world, partly because I started out analog. I have a basis for comparison. We lived without TV. We had a party line; it was attached to the wall. We mailed off our film to be developed. Our maps were paper. I took typing in high school. It was a different time, for sure. And this is a different time. And the time to follow will be different. Better? Maybe. It's hard to see what labor-saving devices may be in the offing, especially since there's not much labor being done at home anymore.

Of course, we also could be bombed back to the Stone Age, too. And then who'd need a washing machine. Is it possible? Sure. Is it likely? Hard to tell. I bet no one thought an arch duke dying in Serbia would lead to two world wars killing hundreds of millions of people a century ago. Talk about a lifestyle change. But I guess that's the whole point of the future. You never know. You just muddle along doing the best you can, trying to have a little fun along the way, and hoping you did the right thing by investing in that mutual fund. Sometimes it works out, sometimes it doesn't.

I do know this. We had a hard rain yesterday. Two inches fell. The wind was fierce. There was lightning, too, but not close. It's cool this morning, the cats are hungry, my wife's asleep, and the sky is clear. There's shopping to do and yard work. A friend is in town and may stop by. I'll stand on the porch and watch the pasture. The world will turn, and I'll make my way through it one step at a time.

Out with the Old, In with the New

Tuesday, April 11, 2017

Our weekend. Popped into a downtown hospital, wife picked up new knee, got it installed. Two days of field trials and we were released to come home yesterday. Wife is currently napping in favorite chair. So far, the recovery time for this new knee is exponentially faster than her last new knee. She's motoring around in her walker, getting dressed, getting coffee, pointing out areas to me that need cleaning. It appears that everyone who said they'd offer up a prayer did so, and to good effect. Much thanks.

We'll see how she feels, however, after the physical therapist gets here this afternoon. Therapy is always the hard part, but she participated well at the hospital and seems totally on-board with the program. This is not to say there's no pain or discomfort, but it does seem slight and a better alternative to the previous situation, which was bone on bone. Kudos to our surgeon who is constantly working to refine and improve his techniques. Mission accomplished.

We had several visitors over the weekend. My wife's brother and his wife stopped by as did my wife's friend of longstanding and her husband. The two girls met when they were seven and they're older than that now. Both families brought flowers. In the meantime, other friends have offered helping hands if we need them, and friends of nearly equal long standing are coming over this afternoon to bring dinner and visit. That will be nice and a pleasant way to end our first full day at home with our new hardware. There is still some length to the journey, but we've made a good start with hands to steady us along the way.

Two Dogs[1]

Friday, April 14, 2017

I have a brief, inconsequential Tommy Chong story. It was the early 1970s. He and Cheech Marin were appearing at Liberty Hall. Their first show there as their careers took off. I offered to give him a ride to the after-show party. He agreed. We stopped by my house to pick up my wife and another couple. We all piled into our 1969 VW. Tommy was in the front seat with my wife in his lap and our friends in the back. That's it. The entire story. There was a party, we had fun.

I guess the take-away is that Tommy Chong was nice and not at all offended that he had to ride with my wife in his lap in a cramped VW. Of course, she's a fine-looking woman, but still. He was pleasant to our friends and even talked to us when we got to the after-show party. He struck me as a decent human being having fun doing what he was doing. I always thought of that night every time I saw him on TV or film. Tommy Chong laughing and smiling in the front seat of my VW.

Now there's a rumor that he's gone. It's not true, but still it makes me sad. I hope he's had a good life. I know we did. We still see our friends from that night. They live just down the road along Rebecca Creek. We're friends and our kids are friends and we still talk about the night we took Tommy Chong to a party. For all the laughter and joy he and Cheech spread out over their careers, we always remember the night he gave it to us for free. It was a nice gift to give to strangers.

---

[1] This refers to a rather famous Cheech and Chong skit about Ralph and Herbie

Across the River

Thursday, April 20, 2017

My wife is up and around after her knee surgery, but as she walks she swings her right leg around like Long John Silver. I know this is a bad habit and I would like it to stop. She needs to walk heel to toe with her foot pointed straight ahead. But there's pain involved and that's personal. The physical therapist, who takes the long view, reminds me of that. She also points out that it has been less than two weeks since the surgery and the patient's progress is remarkable. I understand all that, but the scenarios are still out in front of me and I know that leg swinging ends in a bad place.

Yesterday morning there was a glimmer of hope. We were preparing to leave the house for the follow-up visit to the doctor. I was gathering up the dog, and my wife was walking past me to get into the car. As she walked by and I looked down at the dog, I noticed her feet out of the corner of my eye. It was heel to toe. Slight, but there. The brain was doing what it preferred to do, and her body was going along. There was a limp, but the walking motion was pure. It made me feel good.

It was one of those little stone-of-hope moments we find as we make our way across the river of life. A place to step and stay out of the raging current. I've been accused on occasion of making them up, being overly optimistic. I prefer to think I'm simply observant and know when good things are happening, even when they're little. Granted, they may not always work out. But I prefer walking to the light rather than sitting in the darkness because you never know where the journey will take you.

Things that Go Bump in the Night

Friday, April 29, 2017

Early this morning I felt a sting in my left forearm. It felt suspiciously scorpion. I checked the sheets and blanket but found nothing. Since I was awake, I lay down on the couch and read a bit before returning to my slumbers. This morning, in the light of day, I searched the bed once again. And there, between the pillows was the culprit: *Centruroides vittatus* – the striped bark scorpion.

It occurs to me that scorpions have live birth and carry their young on their back. I'll check to see if I can find any youngsters, if there were any. For all I know, I got bit by a baby. I've got a black light, so I'll break it out before bed tonight to see what's up. The remaining question is how are they getting into the house? I have my suspicions and later today I'll see what I can do to block their egress.

And speaking of things that sting, I've also discovered an inordinate number of wasp nests around the house in places where they've never been. I've been dispatching those, too. I'm good with nests up and away and out of sight, but on the porch where we congregate they are verboten. Meanwhile, I'm left to figure out what sort of message Mother Nature is sending. I wish she'd just learn to write letters. The signs are hard to divine.

Ordinary Things

Tuesday, May 16, 2017

My wife and I went for a walk yesterday. We held hands. Went out our gate and down Back Forty road into the park. It wasn't a long walk because it was impromptu and she still had on her house slippers. We stopped where the road turns into the main body of the park. She said she wanted to follow that road, tomorrow. Today she was just showing it to me. Her new knee is better and she's ready to see the world.

We also took a drive yesterday. I can remember when my parents did that on Sunday afternoons. We'd take a drive just to see the countryside. Sometimes they had a destination in mind, but usually it was just an excuse to get out of the house. Our drive, yesterday, had a purpose. We went to Blanco to check on an order at the little Sears store, and then stopped at the Sonic for cherry limeades. We used to go on similar outings when we lived in Alvin. It was a nice summer ritual, a drive through the country followed by a refreshing drink.

We ended the day on the back porch. She loves the laser light I put in the flower bed. It comes on at dusk and stays on for four hours. The little lights move on the leaves of grass as they blow in the wind and some of them even make their way up into the big trees in the pasture. It is pretty magical. I'm happy that a simple thing such as lights on leaves gives her pleasure. It's hard to find a good gift, and nice when it shows up in the simplest of gestures.

Adult Learning, Monday

July 3, 2017

For the longest time, I've viewed the bandana as an artifact of a bygone era. A large, colorful hankie for me, but nothing I would wear. That was until last week. I was working on an outdoor project and as the sun beat down I began to cover more and more of my body. The neck seemed problematic. My large brim hat covered a bit, but not as much as I'd like. Then I remembered two bandanas gifted to me by a friend.

I pulled one out. Tied it on, and I was set. A little bit later, I dipped it in some rain water, and I started to cool. Now I know how old men in Texas work outside in the summer. They have a big hat and a bandana. Okay, they wear other clothes but those two are essential. I even wore it to the store when my wife needed an errand run. It no longer seemed an affectation. It was what I wore to work, and it's what I will wear going forward when I mow or weed or do anything that requires my presence while the summer sun is shining. Protect the neck and stay cool.

I think this is what people call a paradigm shift. It's odd when it happens, but satisfying. I was locked into a view of something, and then, in an unexpected turn of events, my view changed. The bandana gained a purpose and I understood it. I wish life would be a little more straightforward, but I think it prefers we arrive at our own conclusions even if they are a day late and nearly a dollar short. It does offer hope, however, because even at an advanced age, I can still learn. Giddy-up.

Lessons Learned

Friday, July 7, 2017

The other day, as I worked on my home improvement project, I put a screw in my mouth to hold it while I screwed in its sibling. I immediately removed it, however, because somewhere in the dark recesses of my mind came the admonition, probably from my parents, that it was dangerous. One cough or sneeze and then the screw would become a picture on an X-ray. Swallowed. Of course, I've never heard of it happening to anyone, but it was a potent image and seemed reasonable.

On the "this-actually-happened" side, my wife once worked for an orthopedist. He treated a patient who had his arm broken while hanging it outside his car window. A piece of road debris flew up. Thus, I no longer rest my arm on the windowsill of a rolled down car window. I've also seen people slip and fall on the decks of wet pools, so I don't run there, either. And once, as my father and I drove along Hempstead Highway, I watched a mower across the road hurl a big rock right at us. It came in slow motion and missed, and we were lucky.

I come well equipped to understand the evil that can befall me if I'm careless or just plain unlucky. It has made me cautious. I understand consequences, and I can play them out like a chess game in my head. Before I make a move I look around. It's a hard way to go through life, though, because on occasion you have to rush ahead. That's how I met my wife. I ran after her, literally. Down the street. Caught her at the corner. Got her name and number. Called the next day. That was 48 years ago. I have to say, it was a good move on my part, and a nice way to learn that risk has its rewards.

Part 2: We Go Public

E ven though I didn't talk about it much in my public writings, my wife's dementia symptoms were slowly growing more noticeable. In late 2016, we made our way to Houston to visit a neurologist at the University of Texas Medical Center. After several visits and multiple scans, the frontotemporal diagnosis came down although we'd probably heard it before, we just weren't listening.

This time, perhaps the neurologist presented it with such clarity it was hard to ignore, or maybe we were simply ready to accept the diagnosis. At any rate, we knew. He then sent us to the Nantz Alzheimer's Institute where they were doing a study on FTD. More scans were done, and more details were revealed about the disease and its mechanics. This went on through the first half of 2017. Even then I kept it to myself, in terms of my public writing, preferring to focus on the upbeat. Besides, until this point she still had been functioning at a relatively high level, and could mimic the actions of those around her.

In August of 2017, however, the elephant in my life came to occupy several rooms, and I needed the release. We'd just taken the keys to the car away from her, and she was starting to do odd things in the kitchen. She knew the form of the activity but was losing sight of the dangers. I'd also begun talking to our insurance company about activating her long-term care insurance. Life was piling on, and I was bending.

So, I unburdened. Told the story. Let it all out. Of course, most friends and family already knew what was up, since they'd seen my wife on a regular basis, and we'd talked with them about her situation. But other friends were less well informed, especially ones we only saw periodically around music and other social activities. The public postings changed that.

The unexpected outcome was discovering how many other people were dealing with similar situations. Dementia, disease, loss. You name it. It was all there. They talked. They told me of mothers, fathers, loved ones dealing with dementia. And there were also those who had lost or were losing loved ones to diseases such as cancer, ALS, or MS. Slow deaths. It seemed we were all in the same boat, cycling through the stages of grief with each progression of our respective diseases.

Out of Order 1

Tuesday, August 8, 2017

Went to Houston last Friday to have a PET scan with an experimental tracer to look for inflammation in the brain. It will be overlaid on a detailed MRI they took several weeks back. I'm part of the control group for a study being conducted at the Nantz National Alzheimer Center at Methodist Hospital. Supposedly, I have a healthy brain. Unfortunately, they found me because my wife was there as a patient in the same study.

A little protein in her brain called *tau* has decided to misbehave. Its normal job is to build and rebuild microtubules to hold axons and dendrites together in neurons so the brain can process information. Some of her tau, unfortunately, has more phosphorus than it needs, so the little proteins hang around but don't do any work. Brain cells die. Words die. They have no idea why it's happening or why these dodgy little particles decided to congregate where they did. One thing is clear: eventually they'll be everywhere and the brain will cease to function, and that will be all.

That's a little difficult to process and sometimes I feel like the subject of Edvard Munch's "The Scream." I was pissed off all day yesterday and couldn't shake it. But then I try to step back and realize I'm hardly the only one. Family and friends close to my heart are dealing with ALS and MS and cancer. And most of my friends have lost loved ones to various ailments. I think they call it the human condition. So, my job, as I see it, is to hold her hand, listen to music, and just be there. She may not have all the words at the tip of her tongue[2], but she has the thoughts and we've been together for more than 48 years and a look can mean a lot. It will be hard, but we'll get through this as we have other trials. Together.

---

[2] It may seem odd to say that we continued to talk, but we did. She had to spell words when she lost them, but generally she could do that, and I could understand what she wanted.

Out of Order 2

Wednesday, August 9, 2017

It's interesting to watch people talk to my wife when they have no idea of her condition. They make the inevitable small talk while she watches and smiles. Sometimes her reply matches the conversation and sometimes it's slightly off, and sometimes it's wildly off. I only have the vaguest sense of how much she actually understands. I imagine it's more than I think, or at least I hope it is. She's good at reading facial expressions and she understands the speakers' tone and sentence structure. It's her language that's left the building.

Friends who know her and of her condition speak directly and slowly and look her in the eye and let her try to reply. They might probe a bit to gain an understanding of her meaning. The "W" words, "what", "when", and "why" are of no use, however, so their probing is circuitous at best. Still, friends of long standing give it a try. Lately she's taken to holding people gently by the face and telling them with great intensity that she loves them. No one seems to mind, and they reciprocate with kind looks and words of love in return.

I wish there was some way to fix this, but hers is a relatively rare condition and Alzheimer's is more prevalent. The research dollars go where the most people live. Still, the neurologists at the Nantz Center are working on her condition and when trials come up we'll probably be eligible. They're also getting ready to do some genetic testing as part of her study. It will be interesting to see what that reveals. In the meantime, we've got our daily routine, tons of good music, and once in a while when we're sitting in our chairs in the front room she'll reach over, take my hand and say, "I love you."

Out of Order 3

Thursday, August 10, 2017

When I was first coming to grips with my wife's condition, I kept thinking: *I want her back.* I missed the give and take of daily conversations, the advice, the pushback, the sensible voice, the not-so-sensible voice, the help with planning the day, the week, the month's adventures. When you have a partner, you talk more than you realize about more than you realize. All of that was leaving.

It would be so easy to continue down that rabbit hole. To tell myself, *this isn't the woman I married*, and maybe end up in a place of bitterness. But that's not where I wanted to go. After all, in one sense, she wasn't the woman I married the day after we got married. Time slips by. People change, we grow up, babies come, jobs come and go. The stress of living waxes and wanes, tempers flare, words fly, hugs are tendered, kisses given, there are moonlit nights on the beach, vacations, graduations, more babies. Life. No. This is still the woman I married. We're just in another one of those phases that make up our life together.

I'm a lot more comfortable now with this new situation. We've developed a routine as we bump along on the ocean of life trying to make our way, safely, to the final port. The day is divided into nice segments: post office, lunch, maybe a trip to the store, dinner. When I'm outside for too long, working, often she comes looking for me. She'll stand there with a sweet smile, watching, happy to know I'm there. She does the same thing when she climbs the stairs to my office to sit and watch. She likes to hear me play the guitar and sing like I did when we first met. So, it seems fitting to wrap things up the same way.

Out of Order: CODA

Friday, August 11, 2017

During one of the meetings with a neurologist in Houston earlier this year, he remarked that he typically saw my wife's problems in patients who had suffered a traumatic brain injury. It was an offhand comment. In discussing this with one of my wife's Louisiana cousins, I discovered that at the age of eight she was involved in a one-car accident. She hit the windshield headfirst and broke it. I've mentioned this to each of her doctors but they seem singularly unimpressed. But maybe it was a fact they filed for future reference.

As for myself, I'm going to keep reading and talking, partly because you never know and partly because it will help me feel less of a helpless toad. This probably explains why I finally watched the movie "Concussion" about Dr. Bennet Omalu's work. At its heart it's about him fighting with the NFL, but for me it was a medical mystery. So, I read his paper. Lots of incomprehensible stuff, but lots of familiar words, too. My take-away? Don't get hit in the head, especially a lot. It made me think of my mother who didn't allow her four boys to play football. I got some in during my Navy stint, but nothing long term. Thanks, Mom.

I passed the lesson along to my sons, who played baseball and basketball. My grandson became a baseball player as well. He's in Long Island this weekend showing off his stuff to college coaches prior to his senior year. Reports last night indicate he did well. Good velocity, a plus curve, and outstanding mound presence. I'll try to explain it to my wife, but most likely she'll be happy because I'm happy, without understanding why. Although, the brain is a mysterious thing and maybe the synapses will line up and fire in order today and she'll get it. It's worth a try and it certainly won't hurt. She loves her children and grandchildren and that's some big medicine.

A Reflection, Tuesday

September 12, 2017

I've decided, if you live long enough, you're going to see lots of memorable things and some of them will be bad. During my life, there have been wars, assassinations, and riots. I can tell you where I was during most of them. My historical life started at Camp Pendleton watching Marines get ready to depart for Korea. I was in a high school English class when President Kennedy was killed. I was driving home from a doctor's appointment on 9/11. And those are just the public disasters. I have a goodly list of private heartaches.

But, in amongst the dark is some light. There's the apartment in Hyattsville where a friend and I celebrated the Dodgers' first World Series win over the Yankees. The trailer in Valdosta where I saw Neil Armstrong walk on the moon. The showroom in downtown Houston where we stood and watched the first space shuttle land. And of course, there are the private joys. My wedding. Three children. Two grandchildren. College graduations, my own, my wife's, my kids'.

All things considered, life's been good. For that I'm thankful. It only takes a quick look around to realize it's not that way for everyone. Overall, I try to have the bad inform me, and the good guide me. Basically, I want to walk to the light. The dark is too depressing. Although, I must confess that even when you're walking toward the light you should be careful because it's bright and you can step in a hole. I've done that a time or two. I imagine I'll do it again. It's also possible to simply stop and enjoy it and do nothing. It's important to keep moving forward. Otherwise, as my mother used to say, "The road to hell is paved with good intentions."

Once More with Summer

Tuesday, September 19, 2017

The false fall has disappeared. We're back to muggy mornings and hot afternoons. September in Texas. My grass is suddenly a little long in the tooth, which means mower time. Usually, I keep it cut before the seed heads appear. My weekend trip to Houston to watch college football got in the way. That's okay; our civic garden club only has one member and it's me. I'm giving myself a pass.

Speaking of gardens, I should tend the one off the back porch. One of my lavender plants bit the dust. Its feet got wet during Hurricane Harvey, and it met an untimely demise. They fail to see the benefits of abundant moisture. My wife shows it to me every chance she gets. I have no idea why I don't just reach down and pull it up, but I just agree with her and say I'll do it later. She's good with that, and I have no idea why. I guess after 47 years she knows it will happen sooner or later.

Meanwhile, little pots of seedling Texas trees are appearing all over the place as my arborist son collects his seeds. He has a pink Turk's cap in among the trees, because he knows I like Turks caps. I'm anxious to get one in the ground and have it start blooming. We'll have to wait until next spring, but it should be interesting. I also have a packet of coral vine seeds I picked up during a visit to my sister-in-law's home. She said the plant came from one we used to own. It's a nice symmetry to bring it back home. I need to get those potted. Then I can spend the winter scouting locations and dreaming of pink blossoms and green leaves.

A Day on the Road

Saturday, September 23, 2017

Yesterday was one of those days. A day of travel that unraveled slowly, over time, tiny delays adding up, bit by bit, until nerves were frayed and chocolate and red wine were the only solutions. It started at the doctor's office where a quick visit turned into a form-filled nightmare. A new computer system required new pieces of paper with new signatures and no one had an explanation as to why. Then, on the way to our post-visit lunch, came the realization of forgotten items at home.

Lunch was eaten, steps retraced, and 90 minutes wasted. Our well-planned trip of sequential steps had become an inconvenient series of do-overs. We were now late for our planned trip into Houston to visit our daughter. Traffic was heavy leaving Austin, all the way to Bastrop. Just as we cleared the town and hit the 75 mph speed limit, traffic stopped. Dead. Down came a life-flight helicopter. We waited. I was good with that. One such rescue chopper had plucked my wife to safety in 2015 after her accident. I hoped that this person's situation turned out as well. Back on the road, 45 minutes later, only to find Interstate 10 clogged as only it can be clogged.

At Brookshire we hit another stop on the Interstate. This time it was to take a look at a pick-up in a ditch. Every car on the road had to look. We arrived at our daughter's house three hours later than planned, tired, edgy and sick of the car and traffic and roads in general. The first hugs helped, the dinner salad with chicken even more, but chocolate bars with red wine really turned the trick. Heartbeats returned to normal, nerves were less frayed, and the ship of the world righted itself. Light conversation, a bit of TV, and we were off to bed. As I passed her, Meadow the Cat took a swipe at my foot, as though a cat claw was the perfect way to end a day. Symmetry.

Lullaby and Good Night

Tuesday, September 26, 2017

It rained in the night. I missed it. All that's left is the tell-tale drip off the roof into the gutters and a few puddles on the drive. There's more coming, however, at least according to the forecast. I'll stick around and see what happens. It's a day of no events according to my trusty smartphone. Watching for rain should be easy. I'm at the stage where I like to do that sort of taxing work, watching for rain.

I probably need more exercise, however. I'm pretty sure watching for rain doesn't count. All the doctors ask: How much exercise do you get? I always tell them I walk around a lot and my office is upstairs, but I think I'm underperforming to be honest. I've also been advised by my counselor to get more sleep. The plan we discussed yesterday is fairly appealing. Turn off the smartphone at night, create a buffer zone of quiet before bed, and then get up every morning at the same time. Reading books is a big part of the plan. I'm all in. Last night it was Harvey Penick's *Little Red Book*.

Today I woke up a little earlier than planned, but I did as instructed and dozed until the selected waking hour. Felt like old times, when I had to be at work. There's a lot to be said for a schedule. We'll see how it progresses. I have a list of books I want to read, and it will be good to get back at it. I prefer non-fiction, but a little make believe never hurts. I have some Neal Stephenson titles I want to read. Yeah, sci-fi. I just wish there was a local bookstore nearby. It's a long drive in to Austin.

Something Found

Wednesday, October 11, 2017

Tuesday is trash day and my wife rolls the can to the curb at the crack of dawn. I had a full bin in my office and missed the departure time. I had to walk it out to the street. After I dumped it in and turned to leave, I noticed a piece of paper by the park fence across from our place. I went to retrieve it as part of my anti-litter campaign. Before crumbling it up, I read it. It was a birthday greeting to a father from a daughter, dated 10-13-04.

> Daddy –
>
> You have changed a lot in the past year – for the better.
> You're leaner, meaner, and overall fantastic dad.
> I hope you have a _relaxing_ year.
> I'll always be here for support…
> Happy birthday.

There's a name she signed, but I'll leave it out. I found the card touching. A father making the effort, a daughter recognizing it. He saved it. The card. Probably to remind him of the hard times, and what it's like to work through them. I don't know how the card came to be separated and make its way down our street, but it did. I hope it was because the new dad became the normal dad and he no longer needed a reminder, and the ensuing thirteen years of good memories pushed the old card down and out of sight.

In any case, I'm going to save it because I like the thought of a child having faith in a father and vice versa. If anyone is going to stick with you, it should be family. The compliment she gave him is particularly nice. It recognizes his work, but acknowledges the fight may still be ongoing. It's easy when someone is in trouble to be critical and give advice as if they don't realize things have gone wrong. It's much harder to offer the compliment, but it's probably more important. It's the little stone upon which a new life can be built. A bright word of encouragement. Here's hoping her daddy got it done.

On the Road to Happy

Saturday, October 14, 2017

I like to write a few words every morning, but sometimes it's hard. Sometimes I rummage around in my random thoughts and the only things available are Sad or Angry. More than enough of those two to go around, so I try to steer clear. But the brain is a funny thing, and it keeps offering them up as if I don't really understand how satisfying it would be to give in and go with them. Believe me I do. I've done it enough times.

I guess one of the benefits of age is coming to an understanding of the bigger picture. The entire trip. I've spoken words in anger enough times to know they linger, and that regret is only a partial salve. There are things you can't unsay or unsee. There's a reason they say "silence is golden." It's rare. Of course, all of this is easier said than done and sometimes emotions just get stripped bare and *boom*, off everyone goes. Sadness is a little different. Basically, it robs the world of color and chases joy out of the room. It's a moody old knob.

Meanwhile. Happiness stands there in the corner, tapping its feet, looking at its watch and wondering when the hell you're going to wake up. Your kids are in town, a niece is here from California, and there's a big family reunion today. Hurrah. Happiness wants to party. All in all, it seems a better choice. Being sad and angry won't make anyone well or cure what ails them. And if someone needs a guide to the Promised Land a happy one might serve them better. So, that apparently is how you get to Happy. Cool. Let's do this.

Links in the Long Chain

Monday, October 16, 2017

We had a party Saturday that was several hundred years in the making, depending on how far back on the family tree you want to go. In this case we picked the pair of great-grandparents born in the late 1800s who lived in Johnson City and raised three daughters and a son. They got married, had children, their children had us, and so on. They've been the focal point of every reunion I can remember and I'm getting up there. The great-grandfather in question passed away when I was two but his wife lived until I was 22 and she knew a lot of my cousins.

It was an afternoon of love and food and stories. Good for the spirit. My cousin made picture boards for each of the family groups and folks brought their collections to make them whole. We even spent time updating the electronic family tree with marriages and births of the newest arrivals. It's easy to lose track when everyone is off having children, keeping jobs, and just living life. Most of the cousins who knew the great-grandparents are doing their best to keep their own children involved. Applause to them.

I hope they make it, but I know how difficult it is to keep track of everyone. I can remember our trips home to San Antonio as a child and how bewildering it felt to have all my father's cousins floating around, hugging and laughing and kissing, but they were patient and gradually it fell into place for me. Now, we're trying to pass it along and hope the new children understand and gain the great sense of belonging we feel. The sense that no matter how hard the path, there will always be someone there to hold your hand and wish you well. I think they call that love.

Something Old, Something New

Wednesday, November 8, 2017

Winter has returned. It stopped by about three weeks ago, killed off a few leaves, and left. It's back now. Apparently, we're at the high for the day with lows to come, and rain. Rain will be nice. I hope that promise is kept. Winter rain is good, because it sticks around. No evaporation to speak of. Just water that percolates down. It helps the trees, because they've given up on leaves, and just store the water in their trunks. Smart.

An old friend from high school stopped by yesterday. It was his first time to visit the house. We went out to lunch and then spent the afternoon on the back porch trading stories, remembering escapades and catching up on plans. It was a good afternoon and it was nice to hear his voice again. He's been living on the East Coast but is starting to make the swing back to Texas. It will be nice to have him closer to home. He's got stories to tell and I have time to listen.

Earlier in the month a new friend stopped by for the first time along with his wife. We talked baseball, music and kids. We had a shot of whiskey, too. Took in the view and said we'd do it again. That will be nice. It's always good when friends stop by, new or old. They make the house a home, alive. The conversations flow into the corners, cover the pictures, intertwine lives and give the place a presence. It creates a tapestry that I can look at from time to time that helps me believe that life is still good.

One Day at a Time

Thursday, November 9, 2017

A quarter inch of rain, 46 degrees, overcast skies, and less than ten hours of daylight. Winter. That's what we have right here in our little town. With the coming cold, I outfitted the big kennel with blankets, inside and out, and put it on the leeward side of the building. The porch cats made it a home. Good for them. It's a community effort. I assume that they included the little black kitty. I might need to make her a separate abode since the other two are littermates.

Timmy the dog has no such worries. His kennel sits on the floor of our bedroom. He's always air-conditioned or heated. He spends most of his days on the back of the couch by the windows that look out over the pasture. He always sleeps facing in, however, because he wants to be totally aware of any movement within the house that might involve food. If either my wife or I journey into the kitchen Timmy is right there in case we drop something. It makes me feel slobbish, as though I drop food all the time. Maybe I do. Otherwise, how did Timmy get trained? On a side note, I still miss Ernie the dog, our little dachshund, but that's a story for another time.

I have no idea what I'm going to do today. Seems as though I've embarked on the life of a profligate. Most likely I'll work on some of my volunteer projects, pay a bill or two, pick my guitar, and read a book. That seems a totally useful spending of time, particularly the latter. Of course, we'll go get the mail which involves a five-minute drive, both ways. I wonder if the universe views all this as a total waste. Most likely, not. After all, the dung beetle spends his day rolling poop into a ball. Of course, his might be the more valuable contribution, so I should probably be less judgmental.

61

Moving on Down the Road

Monday, November 13, 2017

I've hit lots of bumps in the road. Sometimes, I glide right over them. Sometimes, they blow out a tire. Sometimes, they send me down an entirely different road. My reaction has usually been one of acceptance, of, *Okay, let's see where this leads.* I trace it back to my family being constantly on the move as a child. Getting upset about leaving somewhere changed nothing. The only thing to do was embrace the future.

But I've noticed a change over the years, particularly when it comes to setbacks. They generate more anxiety. I guess it's because I'm unsure how much road is left to get back on the right or better track, and the future seems a lot more immediate and perilous. Of course, there's no actual way of knowing how much time is left, but that's the rational mind talking to the hyperactive, more panicky spirit side. The best bet, I think, is to move along as though there are lots of tomorrows because getting upset never really solved anything.

Back in 2010 when an overly enthusiastic tree trimmer got hold of my big oaks, I thought I'd die. But seven years on they look pretty good and in another seven years they'll look even better. I worked with them and took it a year at a time. That's probably a decent approach to anything. Do what you can and take what comes. In the end, there's always a soft wind, a warm sun, the sound of running water, and the beauty of a flower to carry you through.

Road Trip

Monday, November 20, 2017

It was a road trip weekend to New Orleans that started on Thursday. We made an overnight stop to visit my wife's relatives in Louisiana on the way there, and then powered through the return in one day on Sunday. Coming home, with meals and bathroom breaks, it took us about ten hours. The drive was relatively easy; we had one major slowdown over the Atchafalaya as they cleared an accident, but that was it. There was sun all the way and we sailed right along.

In days past the trip would have been an opportunity for my wife and I to talk, hash over the weekend's events, chat about our plans for the coming week, and just visit. But her disease has changed all that. We mostly rode in silence, listening to music, holding hands, lost in our thoughts. Old sights along the road would occasionally stir her memories and she'd call them out and usually I knew what she meant, but sometimes not. It didn't really matter; all I had to do was listen and smile in agreement.

She seemed to enjoy New Orleans. There was a touch of rain on Saturday evening as we watched the football game, but otherwise, it was cool and clear for the weekend. Our hotel, with its European charm, was in the French Quarter, and since her knee replacement in April she's able to get around without the constant pain of a bum knee. So, we were able to walk the streets, get beignets at Café Du Monde, and enjoy the sights. It helped that old friends were there as well to hold her hand, ease anxieties, and make life feel slightly more normal. In the grand scheme of things that's a pretty nice outcome.

'Tis the Season 1

Tuesday, November 21, 2017

Yesterday morning I was greeted with hard, cold temperatures in the 30s, and today it's a spring chill in the 50s. I think we're in a pattern where the temperatures will go up and down within that range. Good. Winter. It will get me ready for the holidays. Back in the days when I worked in publishing, I used our annual December trip to New York for a sales meeting to set my holiday clock. It was all about the East Coast cold and Rockefeller Plaza with its giant Christmas tree.

They've started putting up Christmas decorations in our little town. The park is adorned, the light poles festooned, and the Courthouse draped in lights, ready to be lit. All of this will have, as its counterpoint, the yard at the PEC where all the oak trees will be covered in lights so dense it will be hard to look at them without shielding your eyes. The lighting ceremony will happen this weekend after we've all had a chance to digest our Thanksgiving feasts and do the dishes.

Our house will join the party, too. Our lights are neatly labeled in bins in the attic. They'll come out, go up, and we'll be ready. Previously, I would have resisted while my wife pestered, but that's all changed. I'm in charge of the memories now. She liked the house lit, so it will be lit. I'll even drag down the Christmas tree and all the ornaments. She'll enjoy decorating, I'll enjoy watching her do it, and happiness will come to our house.

Grateful

Thursday, November 23, 2017

There's a hard cold on the land this Thanksgiving morning. It's heavy robe weather. I've got it on, and I'm ready. I've been outside to stand on the porch and soak it all in. The sky is light blue with a touch of pink as the sun gains prominence. And the cats are hungry. I left their food dispenser out overnight and it looks as though the raccoons cleaned it out.

Last night I covered my pink Turks cap sprouts in the flower bed by the garage to protect them from the cold. I left the ones under the big trees alone along with the ones in the back lot. We'll see how they all do come spring. The little lacey oak sprout in the back is up to about ten inches and looking strong. The youngest son says the lacey oaks are pioneer trees, which means they can go it alone. That's how they gain ground in this dog-eat-dog world.

Later this morning we'll head out for a Thanksgiving meal with my brother and his wife. I tried explaining it to my bride and she smiled and nodded, but I can only hope she understood. Doesn't really matter. She'll be happy when we get there. In the meantime, there are still blessings to count; they should be counted, and they will be. I could enumerate them, but it would be a long and semi-tedious list. It would start, for instance, with the view of a fat mockingbird sitting on the bare branches of the burr oak outside my office window; run through all the friends and family I still enjoy; and make it all the way through to my grandkids, one of whom will be going to college next year. And, if you're reading this, I'm grateful for you, as well. Peace.

Round Up

Friday, November 24, 2017

There's a nice purple haze over the ground this morning. In contrast, a couple of emergency vehicles just went screaming down the road heading west. And in the pasture in the park the horses are grazing by the barn. Earlier this year the park employees did a massive spray job on the horse pasture to kill off the broadleaf weeds and help the grass reestablish. It worked. The horses seem happy. They have room to roam and there's plenty to eat.

We had a bit of a kerfuffle the other day in the park when one of the Longhorns got out. The park rangers had to shut the gate to Back Forty road right across from our gate. They did their round-up in pickup trucks and even brought in outside reinforcements. I meant to ask why they didn't saddle up the horses. It seemed a perfect opportunity to recreate old ranch life.

As I watched, I wondered how cowboys ever managed a herd of Longhorns. I've ridden in a round-up or two and most of the time the cattle were pretty willing to let even a greenhorn like me on a horse shoo them around. Today's Longhorn, on the other hand, seemed less than interested in anything the truck drivers wanted him to do and those horns gave him a substantial reach. One or two park employees came up on foot but I noticed they stayed well back. I think the Longhorn finally returned to his home pasture out of boredom. Anyway, at some point, things settled down, they opened up the back gate, and the neighbors once again were taking their daily walks through the park.

Lighting up the Night

Saturday, November 25, 2017

They lit the courthouse and popped off fireworks last night. The Christmas season is officially underway. It's the festival of lights, luring tourists like moths to our little town to spend a few coins and enrich the burghers of Johnson City. Last night it was tail lights all the way down to the stoplight as we stood on the porch and watched the pyrotechnic display.

The big draw is the yard filled with the well-lit oak trees of the PEC. They're just across Highway 290 from the Courthouse. Most of them are covered in white lights, but there are blue ones thrown in for a good mix. People of all ages come to see them and take holiday pictures of their families and their children playing beneath the trees. We'll go too, because it's fun.

Today I'll put up my Christmas decorations although the once-young trees I planted back in 2010 are beginning to obscure our house and block the view of our holiday lights, which is okay, because the lights are mainly for me and my wife. I guess people can see them from the road, but they're just ordinary decorations and no cars come trundling down our dead-end street to look at them. That's okay, too. I think the best decorations are personal and if you're aiming to go viral you're probably missing the point of the season anyway. So, I'll string the lights, say a prayer, and get ready for Christmas Day.

A Short Walk

Monday, November 27, 2017

There was a wispy cloud just over the eastern horizon this morning, pink against the bluing sky, looking around the curvature of the earth to catch an early glimpse of the sun. It blew away in the face of the southerly breeze. The trees on the skyline were black and lightless but the grass of the pasture was catching a hint of sun, brown and gold. The air is chill this morning and will only see a moderate rise in temperature throughout the day.

It will be pleasant to be outside, just as it was yesterday morning when my wife and I took a walk up our road then down the fence line toward the main entrance to the park. We passed the horses that stood unperturbed beneath the small oaks in the pasture. As we entered the park a young family went before us, carrying two small chairs for the kids. One of the children kept turning to look back at us and would have fallen if not for the hand of his father holding him up. They stopped in the shade of the big stone barn.

My wife and I walked past them toward the Back Forty road and the entrance to our home. We held hands as we walked. She remarked on the color of the trees. As we entered the yard, she pointed out the Christmas lights I'd put up and expressed her pleasure. I already knew she liked them, because she goes out each evening to look at them when the timers bring them forth. Still, another bit of thank you is always appreciated. We stopped on the porch for a bit as the cats welcomed us back, then went inside to prepare for the rest of our day.

Dashing through the Woods

Friday, December 8, 2017

There's nothing like a little snow to lighten the spirits of a Texan. My youngest son brought me the word last night and I shared it with my wife. There was excitement. We all stood outside and watched the white stuff fall until the cold drove us back inside. Nothing stuck for the first hours; the temperatures throughout the day had been too warm. Then night fell and the temperatures with it. And then the snow fell and it covered, ever so slightly, the ground.

It snowed the day my first-born son came into the world. He was so interested in seeing it that he came two months early. He was just ten inches long and weighed about four pounds and looked like a plucked chicken. He spent his first 30 days in neo-natal ICU. It was still cold when he came home, but the snow was gone. This snow, too, will disappear, probably at first light or at least when the sun has had enough time to deal with the frigid air that brought us all this excitement.

Later today the wife and I will drive to Houston for a company party followed by a family party tomorrow. The roads most likely will be clear by the time we depart but the fields will probably still be white, which will make for some pleasant viewing as we head south. If we could, we'd talk about the time it snowed on us in Alvin on Christmas Eve 2004 and we ended up with a white Christmas. Maybe she'll think about it as we drive. I'll keep my ears peeled to see if she brings it forth.

Going Around, Coming Around

Tuesday, December 12, 2017

The presents are now neatly piled in the corner of my office and it's time to get wrapping. Online shopping is a real boon when you live in the country. Most of the kids don't realize it but we've circled back to the days of the Sears catalog. In the heyday of the catalog, you could buy anything from Sears, including a house. They'd ship it to you and you'd assemble it. I hate to think how I'd handle that, but if that was the best, more affordable choice, I'd probably do okay.

It's amazing to think that Sears was the Amazon of its time, but it was. Now Amazon is opening brick and mortar stores and soon they'll be America's new Sears. Weird how all that goes around. Sears was our go-to store as kids. It was fun shopping there. They sold candy and popcorn and tires and the stores smelled great and there was a lot of excitement. It cooled off as we aged, but it was still pretty strong for a long time. My wife worked at a Sears in Pasadena when we were first married.

I guess, however, when you lose the magic, you lose the magic. They've tried everything to get it back, but nothing seems to work and now they've gone the way of the five and dimes, which gave way to the dollar stores. I guess if all this tells us anything, it's that there's not much new under the sun. It's the same stuff dressed up in different clothes. I mean, really, how many ways can you sell people stuff? Lots, apparently. But, hey, variety is the spice of life, right? Maybe when you're young. Right now, I'd go for a bland diet of easy. But that's just me.

One Day at a Time

Tuesday, January 2, 2018

2017 was a Christmas of discovery. We twice drove to Houston to celebrate. First, we gathered with my wife's family. Brothers, sister, spouses, and kids came together for food, games, and camaraderie. A week later, we went back to celebrate with our Houston children. Presents were exchanged, food eaten, and love reinforced. Both events were quintessential Christmas celebrations, with one exception: it was obvious during the celebrations that my wife had only the vaguest notion of what was happening. On the way home, with her in the car, two days before Christmas, I cried a bit. I thought of other Christmases as a young couple before kids and knew this year could have been one of those, but this year I'd be the only one with memories or a chance to build them.

We forged ahead, however, opened presents, and ate Christmas breakfast. My youngest son came in, having spent the night away, and we opened and shared his presents. Later in the day, my wife insisted we go to the store to get milk. We drove to the closed store. She tried the doors, and came back perplexed. Luckily, a chain drugstore was open. We got milk. Back home I grilled steaks, baked potatoes, and the three of us had a nice dinner. That evening, I was talking to my oldest son, and we remarked on how each day, even a holiday, was the same to his mother as every other day. There was the routine, and things to be done, just like always. My sadness lifted. I realized that holidays, and weekdays, and weekends are all constructs that we layer on top of time to break it into manageable bits. In the end, we live our days and they're all the same, in their essence, one to the other, regardless of how we dress them up.

It wasn't about Christmas, or a holiday or a weekend, it was just about being together. We did it again on New Year's Day. We rose, ate our breakfast, and at ten o'clock drove to the post office where she checked the mail. Later I cooked some ham and black-eyed peas. At one point, as the day wore on, she showed me her phone and its calendar. She pointed at the "one" and the year. I said yes, it's 2018. She repeated the number and smiled and that's how we brought in the New Year, one day at a time.

Teamwork

Friday, February 9, 2018

It's nearly 30 degrees warmer this morning than it was yesterday. Now, that's some Texas weather. We go from ice on the pond to warm enough for golf. Yes, sir. That's how you do it. It started warming up yesterday. Of course, the TV guys say we could have freezing rain by the weekend, but again, Texas. I'm good with it. It still feels like winter and I don't have to drive anywhere except the post office.

Spent a little time pulling dead morning glory vines off the fence yesterday. It was identified as a problem by the wife, and I was tasked with the solution. Fair enough. They probably needed to come down anyway. I think we're looking at several years' worth of dead vines and they are slightly unattractive. I'm about half-way done and should be able to deal with the rest today. My own goal in the dead vine war is to rid us of the ones that grew out into the driveway.

I'm fairly certain she'll circle around to the lantanas next. They're totally devoid of leaves and in a normal year she probably would have trimmed them back already. But these are no longer normal years, and I'm happy she's out walking around checking the grounds. Gives me some semblance of old times. Granted, it's a little hard to have a discussion, given her language difficulties, but we manage with a grimace, a nod, a wink and a kiss as we make our wishes known.

A Time of Planting

Wednesday, February 21, 2018

Went to bed at the appointed hour, woke unexpectedly when a thunderstorm hit. There was thunder, and rain beating against the window, which is a real trick since the window is under a roof that covers over eight feet of porch. Suffice it to say there was wind. I'm unable to sleep when nature is throwing a loud party. To kill time while the storm passed, I poked around and found a cache of pictures in an old desk. It was fun looking at them as I sat there in the semi-dark front room.

A great many of them were from Christmas 2002. The family had gathered at our house in Alvin. These pictures were post-present opening, probably even post-meal. My daughter and I are on film singing a song together. There's one of her pitching a new tent on the back porch, and there are several of the grandson, still new at the time to the family gathering. He was two. He turns eighteen next week and graduates high school in May. There was also a batch of pictures of my wife and I planting a small peach tree at our home here in the Hill Country, ten years later, in 2012. The little tree was about two feet tall. It now stands well over 20 feet and occupies more territory than a peach tree really should occupy. In the years following their arrivals, the boy and the tree both did a good job of growing up.

After the storm passed and the evening grew quiet, I returned to bed. As I slipped off to sleep I waxed nostalgic for the days of the two-year-old grandson and peach tree planting. The former is made easier because there is still a bright future for the young man. The latter, however, fills me with dread and makes me feel like the face in Edvard Munch's *The Scream*, because the only thing remaining for my wife is the death of her brain cells, killed by errant proteins. I have a broad vocabulary to describe how I feel about that, but it's impolite to use it in public and people have troubles of their own, and there's no point in adding to them. Besides, raging against life is pointless. Time passes, children grow old, adults leave, and new children arrive. There's a lot to celebrate. So, I try to remember that anyone can be happy in times of plenty. The real trick is to do it when times are hard.

73

The Plant Tender

Monday, March 12, 2018

Our front porch is full of flower pots. Fourteen, to be exact. In years past they would have all been trundled into the workroom for the winter, waiting for spring. This year I only had to bring in one of them, the ficus, and that always comes into the house. The others were empty, sitting forlorn on the porch, because the tender of the pots is no longer tending them, and the plant tender's husband was new to that game.

Last week as I walked around the porch, I missed those pots full of flowers. So, this weekend I bought potting soil and plants and filled them all up. Impatiens and gardenias, mostly. Little flowers that have brightened our porches and yards for years. The end result is passable, and the plant tender was happy when she saw those results and she gave me a hug. I'm going back for some pea-gravel today and I'm going to look for some Johnny jump-ups. I can't believe I forgot them the first time around.

The partnership of a marriage is an amazing thing and you never realize how many little things it involves until one of the partners is unable to carry on because her progressive aphasia is progressing. I did the Christmas cards this year for the first time and was delighted to discover that my wife had dutifully noted in her little address book who got what cards in what years. I still mess up the birthdays, though, and I need to get better at that. My beautiful daughter-in-law deserves a public apology. I shall endeavor to make amends. Meanwhile, the plants on the porch can remind me of happier times and give the plant tender some small measure of pleasure.

Floats

Friday, March 23, 2018

Before my family moved to Houston in 1963 we lived in Portsmouth, Virginia in a little house with my parents and three brothers. Just down the road and across the street was a drug store with a soda fountain. Occasionally, they'd treat us with a visit to that fountain, and I always got a root beer float. It was the essence of goodness.

When we moved to Houston, I'd go to an A&W root beer stand, located, if memory serves, on Westheimer just down from Voss Road. I always got the same thing, a root beer float. I was newly married one night in 1970 or maybe 71 when my bride and I visited the stand after leaving my dad's house. We pulled in for our order and as we sat there waiting, we realized Johnny Winter was sitting in the car next to us. We waved, or maybe nodded, and I know he smiled at us. Then our floats came and his order came and off we went in our own directions.

I thought of all this because three days ago I bought a six-pack of A&W root beer and two pints of vanilla ice cream and made myself root beer floats. Not all at once, I paced myself. But they sure were good, although, as always, the ice cream melted too fast. I think I should have chilled the drinks, but I was hungry for the taste and the memories. I offered some to my wife, but it didn't ring any bells with her and I knew she wouldn't remember Johnny Winter in the car beside us. So, I ate in silence and remembered the good times.

On the Road to Somewhere

Wednesday, April 4, 2018

Beauty. It's hard to ignore even in the face of the inevitable. Maybe it's what makes facing the inevitable possible. During the years of my father's final slow decline and my many trips to visit, I found it comforting to glide along Interstate 10 with music blasting and the rolling countryside sliding by my windows. This was different only by small degrees from the same trip made with my family back in the 1960s when we travelled Highway 90 to visit relatives, and the inevitable seemed well-nigh impossible.

It's spring now and everything is blooming and my wife notices, although the language to articulate the world she sees has shrunk to almost nothing. Still, I find her going outside to walk around and look and remark in her way at what she's seeing and it's obvious it gives her joy. It's the same with music. The part of the brain that holds on to words and lyrics is tucked away in a hard-to-reach spot, safe for now from the little proteins playing hell with the rest of her brain. Yesterday at the supermarket she stepped away to look at something on a shelf. As I got ready to leave I called to her. She walked toward me as a Top Forty classic played over the radio and I could see she was singing the lyrics. I caught her eye and she smiled. It was something about love.

I can't make sense of why this is happening to her. It just is. There are still pleasures to be had, however. She likes to hold my hand and the music is definitely there. Everything in the yard is either blooming or getting ready to bloom. There is beauty around us, and I shall have it and so shall she, and together we will make our way to whatever end the journey presents, and along the way, there will be smiles.

Another View

Thursday, April 5, 2018

Just out the kitchen window I can see one of the big oaks. There's a spot where a limb used to be. Over the years, I've watched as the old bare wood gradually gets covered by new growth. It's called the callus and it is designed specifically to cover the wound so that new wood will grow around it. Fairly efficient technique, one to be admired; slow, but sure.

Humans do something similar with scars, except we simply replace the old skin with lumpy new skin that smooths out a bit over the years, but never really goes back to its original shape. I think we follow the tree's lead with psychic injuries. There's a loss, an insult, an injury, the mind compartmentalizes it, moves on and surrounds it with new memories. Of course, over the years the hurts and losses pile up, and there's a big collection of lost dogs, lost loved ones, and insults both real and imagined banging around in our minds. It must be why old people tend toward nostalgia; we keep tripping over past loves and losses.

But unlike a tree, we can anticipate a loss and that's where things get tricky. It means there are times when the brain takes a timeout to work on compartmentalizing. It stops thinking about the future and starts tying up loose ends, letting us toy with the emotions of loss so that they don't overwhelm us when it actually happens. But then it begins packing in new memories of good things so that we have something to build on, and the day brightens, and the sun shines, and flowers bloom, the kids call, and a nice song comes on the radio as life in general goes on.

Down among the Pots and Pans

Friday, April 6, 2018

I made caramel sauce the other day. First time. It seems to have turned out okay. Of course, how can you go wrong with a dish that calls for eight ounces of sugar in four ounces of water mixed with heavy cream and vanilla? Seems nigh impossible. I'm going to try it again, because this batch looked a little milky and I think it should be more translucent. Still, it tastes pretty good with a slice of Pink Lady apple.

I also cooked a pork loin. I think it was overdone, but my guests were polite and ate it. I'm going to try that again and this time I'll shorten its stay in the crock pot. That's the nice thing about digital thermometers. You can check the temperature on the fly. Pork needs to get to 145 degrees. If I can get closer to that magic number, next time there might be more juice in the meat when it comes time to slice it on the serving platter.

I wish I had paid more attention when my wife was still able to do all the cooking. She was a brilliant chef although she had a rocky start. Soon after our marriage in the summer of 1970 she cooked up a dish of round steak and gravy where she attempted to thicken the gravy with baking soda rather than cornstarch. At first she didn't know what had happened, but then a call to her mother straightened out the problem. After that, it was all good and the dishes just kept getting better and she fed me well over the intervening years. Now, it's my turn, and I won't let her down. I just wish when I screw something up I could call her to find out where I went wrong.

The Collector

Monday, April 30, 2018

Sometimes I cry, when the load gets heavy. Sometimes I cry, when I grieve for what is lost or what I'm losing. Sometimes. Not all the time. And when I do, it passes. In the glance at a flower. With the touch of a morning breeze. In the glow of a smile. At the sound of a laugh. With the passing of time. The tears. They pass.

It also helps to know I'm not alone. Others carry burdens. Big and small. They're all around me. Close friends, casual friends, distant friends. In the bloom of youth it is possible to forget or not understand that seasons change, and that while life in general proceeds, some bits of it will inevitably stop or change course. When it does, there are usually tears.

I know all of this sounds sort of maudlin, but it helps to write it down. Then it's out there and not in me. I can set it on a windowsill and look at it like the blue glass we collect to catch the sun in the kitchen. Some of it is broken, but even then there is beauty in the parts left behind. Maybe the edges are rounded by the sea and its skin turned to a matte finish. Maybe it's just old, a bit of a bottle dug up. Maybe one day it will just be glass and someone will wonder why we collected it and my tears will have melted away.

A Blast from the Past

Monday, May 7, 2018

I brought my wristwatch out of retirement. Got the battery replaced and strapped it back on my arm. It's a Pulsar that my wife had given me for Christmas back in the 1980s. It features the University of Houston logo on its face, and the minute and second hands glow in the dark. I find it refreshing to check the time with a glance at my wrist rather than pulling a phone out of my pocket. Plus, it's a nice piece of jewelry and looks dressy.

When I first got it, my daily attire was all dressy and included white shirts with French cuffs, wool suits and silk ties. The gold watch looked good peeking out from beneath a starched cuff. I liked dressing up and looking sharp. It seemed a fun part of business. And that included well-shined shoes. I remember a VP of a company where I worked just out of college admonishing a colleague about his tattered shoes. The colleague tried to defend himself by saying it didn't really matter, and the VP said, there are a lot of people who split infinitives, but that doesn't make it right. After that, I kept my shoes shined.

Eventually, business moved away from dressing up, casual Friday became casual every day, people started wearing jeans to church, and no one even knows what it means to constantly split infinitives. I suppose there are grand lessons to be learned from all of this, but I'll be damned if I know what they are. Things just changed as things are wont to do. I could carp about the decline in civilization, but something tells me that a starched white shirt is no more important to the health of civilization than a ruffled Elizabethan collar.

The Day After

Monday, May 14, 2018

I was four years gone from the nest when my mother passed away. This year marks the 50th anniversary of the night in February when the aneurysm in the center of her brain burst. It was a catastrophe for sure. There were still three brothers at home when it happened. Two of the three are up here in the Hill Country now, and the third took his leave in 2005. I guess you could say he's in the Hill Country as well since his ashes are in the Masonic Cemetery just down the road.

The years have distilled my memories of her to their essence. She worked as a nurse, played the piano, went to church, and never forgot that as a child of three, when her mother died, her father put her and her brothers and sisters into an orphanage. That would be classified, I believe, as a hard row to hoe. She graduated high school, however, got her nursing degree and became a Lieutenant in the Navy, which is where she met my father. I believe she would be pleased that my father didn't do the same to his children when she passed. Instead, he remarried and soldiered on, doing the best he could.

Over the years, Mother's Day became the time when I celebrated my wife and her mother, which was fun because both were strong women who appreciated being celebrated. My mother-in-law passed away 20 years ago, although it still seems like only yesterday. And now pieces of my wife's mind are slipping away and Mother's Day to her is simply another day. To celebrate, we went to the store, drove around, and listened to music. I grilled some pork chops for dinner, and held her hand while we watched a little TV. In summary, to quote the lyrics of one of her favorite songs: "Some days a dollar; some days a dime."

In the Current

Wednesday, June 27, 2018

Had a bad morning yesterday. There was anger and shouting. In the middle of it, my wife looked at me with eyes full of fear and incomprehension. All I could do was stop and hold her because there was no way to explain the unexplainable. It was one of those moments when life was just all-around bad. Later that evening we drove to Burnet because she wanted to go somewhere, and the easiest thing to do was just get in the car and drive around. She motions for a direction and I go. Sometimes we end up at an actual destination, sometimes not.

It took me a while to arrive at this equanimous approach. I fought it for a long time, railed against it, in fact. Me being an ass. Hardly a surprise there. But each time, I got a little closer to acceptance until last night when I finally crossed over the bridge. When she came out of the house at about 8:30 p.m. with her purse and my wallet and phone, we just got in the car and headed off. Actually, driving around in the Hill Country after dark is sort of nice. There was a big moon last night and the landscape was well lit. When we got home she was happy and we both went to bed.

I think the best approach to take now is to see what sort of adventures we can have when she decides we need to go. It's that old go-with-the-flow approach. I'm a big fan, even though in this case I found myself fighting the flow with vigor, just as if there had been true intent on her part and I could argue my way out of it. I'm all in now. This is the way the river is running and paddling back upstream isn't an option.

Happy Anniversary

Thursday, June 28, 2018

My wife told me she loved me while we ate dinner at Valian's pizza over by the old Shamrock Hilton in Houston. We were in the back at a quiet table, pretty much to ourselves. It was a lovely moment and I can see it as though it was yesterday. It was the spring of 1969. We married a year later. I'm guessing at that moment of exposure and promise she never suspected that one day her beautiful mind would start melting away and I'd be responsible for her care. But here we are and yesterday was our anniversary, 48 years, and she didn't know it.

Of all the twists and turns we've endured, this is certainly the oddest and possibly the hardest. It's not like I don't know how to care for someone. We raised three kids and I'm pretty sure I got up from the dinner table or a deep sleep more than once to change a diaper or pat someone to sleep with a lullaby. But that was all done with the knowledge that on the morrow they'd become sentient beings who could take care of themselves. In other words, adults. This won't end that way.

I guess that's why you fall in love. Somewhere in the recesses of the mind, along with assessments of earning power and attraction, there has to be the secret calculation that this person will be there for me in times of trouble. They'll pick me up when I fall, kiss me when I'm hurt, and hug me when I'm lonely. At this point, she knows something is up, and I think she knows I'm doing my best to hold up my end. She gives me a lot of random thank-you's and pats on the arm and holds my hand while we sit in our chairs or drive in the car. I wonder if, when she does that, she's somehow thinking back to that day at Valian's. I hope so. I'd like her to think she chose well.

In the Weeds

Tuesday, July 3, 2018

It's hard to believe how cool 77 degrees can feel in the morning, especially after daytime temperatures in the 100s. But it does. And it feels even better with a light breeze. Apparently, there is still enough moisture around to make it all work. I remember back in 2011 when the rain stopped, and the heat built. A 77-degree temperature in the morning was just another hot moment in a dry summer.

Later this morning, I'll be back in the front yard digging up khaki weed. I'm making good progress. As I've dug I've learned about getting the little weed out of the ground. I started by using my big turning fork to loosen the soil all around, and then digging in with a three-pronged small fork at the weed. Then I spotted a small, narrow trowel on sale at the local hardware store. I bought it. And it works. Dig in at the base of the plant, loosen the soil, and the weed pops right out.

As I work I'm reminded of the days when we first moved into our new house and my wife waged a similar war against the grass burrs. Every morning she was out there, sitting in a little chair, digging. It took her almost two years to get them all but get them all she did. I was amazed at her perseverance. I wish she was working with me now because two of us on the front line would really make a difference. But these days she only comes out to look and say, "good, good" before heading back inside to be with whatever memories are still living with her.

At this Point in Time

Tuesday, July 10, 2018

Anger is one of the emotions that sometimes flares, unbidden, in my dealings with my wife and her disease. I thought by now I'd be past it. I'm a semi-bright guy who understands what's happening, and I know how I should behave and why and normally I do. But sometimes, it's just there. Bright and intense and flaming, leading to regret and self-recrimination. And I think, "What the hell, by now I should be approaching at least the fourth of the five stages of grief, right?"

Then it dawned on me: I was dealing with the trees rather than the forest. I was taking each progression of the disease as the new normal and when the stages changed as they inevitably do, I was being yanked right back to the top of the grief cycle. It became clear what my counselor really meant when she said I had to step back: step back, as in *way back*. Further probably than a husband wants to step but where he needs to stand if he wants to make life comfortable for everyone.

Of course, it's hard to be dispassionate when someone you love is dealing with something like this. But it's what's required. Besides, she's not doing any of this on purpose; it's the disease, and that's what I need to keep in the front of my mind. I need to forget for a moment the memories of nearly 50 years and concentrate on the now and the life we're in, because at this point it's all we have, and it will have to do.

One

Thursday, July 12, 2018

Late yesterday evening, I was going to crack open my bottle of birthday bourbon, but realized I had another just like it already open. So, I took one of my little birthday glasses, put two small ice cubes in it and poured a shot. Then I went to my chair, sat down, and sipped my drink. Until it was all gone. It tasted great, as I knew it would. I watched TV for a bit and went to bed.

I've been trying to decide if I should start sipping on a drink every evening. There all sort of reports about the benefits of a single drink of alcohol. And it would help when I fill out forms at the doctor's office. They always ask if you drink alcohol and I say yes, but the frequency question gets me, because they don't have a category for so-seldom-I-can't-remember-the-last-time-I-had-a-drink. With a new nighttime ritual, I could check the "everyday" box.

The downside is that I might get involved in the issue of drinking alone, which I believe is frowned upon. I could claim I'm not alone, my wife is in the other room, but they might say that doesn't really count, you have to have people around. They always talk about aloneness as if it is solely contingent on other people being in the room. But anyone with a lick of sense knows you can be alone in a room full of people. And when your wife is dealing with a debilitating brain disease, that's another kind of aloneness. So, last night when I had my shot I thought of my friends who gave me the gift, and our trip we're going to take today, and the family I'm going to see. And I slept really well.

Boop, Boop, Dit-em Dot-em

Thursday, July 19, 2018

On the wall inside our bathroom over the door connecting it to the bedroom are four ceramic fish. It's a mother and three little fishes. A visitor is unlikely to notice them, but they're there, mute evidence of a long-ago shopping trip. A reminder of a mother and her three children. A little decorative touch that makes a house a home.

I used to find that sort of thing all the time when I came home from work or travel. A little knick-knack on a shelf, a frame on a wall, a throw rug on the floor, a placemat on a table. The intersection of the private lives of married people. She's lost a bit of that freedom now. We can no longer let her drive, which means she's trapped by my desires. We still take her shopping, but it's no longer the private thing it once was, the moment of being alone that everyone needs to maintain their identity. We've moved past that as we adjust to our new end-game reality.

We've added a few new decorative things to the house, but not many. Sometimes I feel as though our house is becoming an archeological site. A collection of mementoes where strangers will have to divine what they mean. Why did they have all those David Winter houses? What do these little pewter cups tell us? And why two china services? Maybe the kids will remember and divide them up for their own homes. Maybe not. Most likely they'll end up in an estate sale or on a table in the back of a thrift store. But maybe that's the whole point of *things*. They work as physical reminders for the living of the good times they had, and when the living are no longer around they go back to being *things* in search of other lives to liven.

The World Around Me

Wednesday, August 1, 2018

It's interesting how the mere act of living these days crowds in and occupies every inch of my brain. There's no space to step back and observe; it's all about doing. I still notice things, but they're noticed incidentally and discarded unless they affect the patient, in which case notes are taken, followed by steps as needed. At the moment, I'm in the process of securing the house of hazards at night: shutting off the stove and microwave, locking the refrigerator. My bride remembers the form of things but not the details, and that's where the devil lives.

Last weekend she spent time at a memory care facility so that I could have a break and get some sleep. The kids understood. It's nice to have family support. We all understand, I think, that we're inching closer to the day when it will need to be longer term, because I'm fairly certain I'm running up to the ragged edge of what can safely be done at home. It's difficult to think that you may have to entrust the care of a loved one to strangers, but maybe that's why we're social animals and make friends. You can work to bring these strangers into your orbit so they will care for your loved one as much as you do, or at least be brought closer to that end.

I think that's why you often see patients' primary caregivers at facilities during the day; they're working to demonstrate a sense of family to the strangers holding their loved ones. The danger is that the caregiver sacrifices all in the name of the patient and then you lose two people rather than just one. Of course, I'm not sure the world would notice or much care. Certainly, close family members would, but after that everyone has their own troubles and the passing of a stranger or even a friend would be noticed and briefly mourned, but life would go on, as life always does.

On Bended Knee

Thursday, August 2, 2018

Yesterday morning my wife complained her foot hurt. I inspected the foot in question and discovered a small cut on the inside of the foot back toward the heel. No idea how it happened. It looked a little aggravated, so I gathered the tools to clean and treat it. There was a basin with warm water. Soap. A clean washcloth. A towel. Polysporin and a bandage. I knelt at her feet and washed them. Patted them dry and applied the medicine.

Periodically, she would say, as I worked, "good, good." It probably reminded her of the pedicures she used to get and enjoy when the world made sense. It reminded me a bit of all the Holy Thursdays I spent in preparation for Easter when the priest washed the feet of twelve members of his congregation. Priests were fairly important people in my childhood universe and seeing one on his knees washing people's feet was unforgettable. The powerful bending before the powerless. Humility.

As I washed her feet I thought of all the miles they trod chasing after kids while I gallivanted around the world on business. Of all the hours spent at the stove making meals that were ready when I arrived home. Of all the time spent in gardens growing the food we would eat. Of dances and walks on the beach. Of paths trod while camping. Of shopping trips. Of life in general. On her feet, on the go. I probably should have been washing them long ago.

The Dying of the Light

Friday, August 3, 2018

A summer's worth of dry is bringing the deer out of the deep woods to drink at the neighbor's well. The windmill brings the water up from the depths and stores it in a big tank, where it drops down to a smaller trough. The deer come in the early evening, stand around drinking, then sidle off to find whatever green they can, some even venturing across the highway into town. On occasion, we find their brethren slain on that highway, victims of men and our machines.

No word on when this latest drought will end. At least we're no longer baking in triple digit heat. Evenings and early mornings are once again cool, and a light breeze makes them delightful. Now, if I could only get enough sleep to enjoy them upon waking. But sleep is a little hard to come by at the moment as we make adjustments to a new reality here at home. My bride's internal clock seems to have sprung a leak, blurring the distinction between night and day.

Unfortunately, my circadian rhythms are still keeping the beat and when the sun rises it's time to shine. Steps will need to be taken to get things back into sync. As I understand it, the brain and the body, primarily the brain, need that sleep to clean out debris, solidify memories, and do the things needed to work properly. I think I see a nap in the future. It's not a perfect solution, but it's sleep and that's good. Per chance I'll dream, taking a restorative trip in the dark of eyes closed against the light, not dying, but getting away. Hardly ideal, but certainly better than nothing.

Going with It

Tuesday, August 21, 2018

If I learned anything during my brief career as a canoeist, it was this. Go where the river wants to go. Anything less will lead to a bent canoe, wet gear, and a ruined back. It didn't take long to translate that lesson to life. It moves at its own unrelenting pace, pushing everything and anything in front of it. It will break you unless you learn to relax and go with the flow and even then it may still break you. Bitching about it may make you feel a little better but it changes nothing.

I am reminded now of that lesson. To say my wife's sleep patterns have changed is a gross understatement. She is just as likely to want to eat lunch at midnight as she is at noon. And we go to the post office twice a day at 10. Light or dark means nothing. I resisted the change, kept my alarm set for six, and ended up a tired, unhappy man. Then I thought of the river and the flow and started going with it.

Now, with the help of my son, and folks I'm fortunate enough to hire, I've turned off the alarm, take my sleep where it comes, and find bright eyed and bushy tailed whenever it arrives. For a long time, in our canoe I had my wife in front and it was the two of us making our way down river. Nowadays we're in a slightly different canoe with some others there to help. We're paddling like hell, watching for rocks, and doing the best we can to stay dry and make it safely to shore. So far, so good.

Better Late than Never

Monday, August 27, 2018

I can remember being sent to the supermarket in the early days of my marriage and feeling like a fish out of water, a man lost in a strange city, with no idea how to get around. There were signs, of course, but they seemed obtuse and meant to purposely confuse. Little things were hidden in odd places because of strange relationships to other things that only my wife and other women and supermarket mavens apparently understood.

Over the years I became a little better versed in the ways of the market and how and why it was laid out the way it was, but it still seemed inordinately difficult to find things. Then came the smart phone and apps and now my favorite store's secrets are revealed. Of course, I still need to wander up and down an aisle looking high and low, but at least I have an aisle and that, my friends, is a spectacular advance.

I've also come to enjoy shopping, which is partly the art of simply looking around. Previously I went in to buy something and that meant I wanted to walk straight to it. No lollygagging. Shopping is the art of going in to buy something and checking out the other things in case you need them at some further point. It's an observational game. These days I even play it in other non-food big box stores. It makes for a much more relaxing trip to the store for sure and means that nowadays, I almost look forward to my trip to the store and my knowledgeable walk around its aisles, picking up my items with assurance and skill, making notes of things to check out later.

Good Night, Moon

Wednesday, September 12, 2018

I do not know the history of our sheets and spreads. Why, for instance, do we have a blue fitted bottom sheet with matching pillow cases, but no top sheet? Where did it go? Was it destroyed in an accident, wiped out by the washer, torn by the dog? Was it stuffed in a mystery place where my wife kept these things? Who knows. It would be really helpful if she could explain it to me, but we're past that. I'm in the rummaging around phase. A voyage of discovery.

I much prefer the days when the sheets got changed and all I had to do was sleep on them. Winter would come, and the flannel sheets would appear with a heavier spread to protect against the cold. Now, I control all that. Not really my wheelhouse, but I'm getting better. My mind still goes blank. I washed a white pillowcase with the red sheets one day. It came out pink. It's a nice color, but even I know things ought to match. So, I went and bought new white pillow cases.

But, we're adjusting. The linens are clean, we sleep moderately well, and life goes on, after a fashion. I'll probably find that blue sheet one day in a place least expected. Or, I could just go buy another set. That, however, feels like cheating. I'm pretty sure it's around here somewhere and will show up. Besides, there's a second set of blue sheets and I stole that top sheet. The hues are slightly different, but when you cover up in the dark, who can tell. That, of course, is a guy's perspective, but that's probably sexist. We'll just say it's practical and let it go at that.

Showtime, Friday

September 28, 2018

We have a rather shapely flame leaf sumac growing between our house and the pasture fence. It's just past its terrible two's. Last year it made real progress until my wife, dealing with some garden memories, decided to cut it down. And she did. The tool she found wasn't made for the job, but it worked. The branches surrendered. She's never abided bare woody limbs and the sumac was no exception. Luckily, the plant has since re-sprouted from the stump, and we're back in business.

She'll probably fuss at me this year after it loses its leaves to cut it again, but I'll resist, although I may do some pruning to make it look a little more tree-like. At the moment, it simply looks like a big shrub. We're past the point where I can use words to explain why I want to leave the tree alone. I'll just have to be on guard to make sure she resists her urge to trim. It will be easier this year because she's hardly ever alone anymore.

As for the sumac, the new trunks and limbs are growing up and out. There's even a slight curve to the trunk as it reaches the point where it can go up. It looks like an Alvin Ailey dancer, body bent, arms reaching up, moving to the music of the spheres, no doubt. I hope this year's show ends with a cascade of brilliant red leaves, but that's up to Mother Nature, and you never know what she has in store.

Dropping Pounds

Tuesday, October 17, 2018

Several months ago my wife's doctor told me I needed to get her weight under control. Previously, I'd been erring on the side of generosity owing to her illness, and maybe because indulging in sweets and eating out made us both feel good. Plus, I'm no chef and rice is easy to cook. The doctor's warning shook me out of my lethargy. It's odd to be told this by a stranger, because my wife's degree is in nutrition from the University of Houston and she was a great and creative cook and she paid attention to what we ate.

Since I can no longer access her nutritional acumen, however, I had to find a dietician. I did. In Fredericksburg. She laid out a plan and off we went. No more candy. No more cookies. One each of the three food groups. More fruit, lean meats, fish. Cut down on snacks. Exercise as much as possible. Voila. Since we started in June, her weight has dropped steadily by nearly 6%. Mine's come down almost 10%. She'd be happy if she understood what we were doing, but she doesn't.

She laughs with glee when I call her to dinner or breakfast or lunch as if I was a Michelin chef, and she eats without complaint or question as we sit together at the kitchen island. There's no discussion of the day's news, plans for tomorrow, gossip about friends, or even any talk about the meal (although she doesn't like raw carrots and she'll gently put her share on my plate). We eat in silence. When we're done the dishes are cleaned, pots and pans scrubbed, and the day continues much as it did before, a long walk to nowhere.

On the Flip Side

Thursday, October 25, 2018

When sleep is plentiful the oddities of my wife's disease are water off a duck's back. The misremembered way to trim a shrub? A small laugh. A misplaced dish? A chuckle. But take away the sleep and I'm left with raw nerves and red eyes. Then the oddities become grim reminders of what's really going on, and I'm ready to rage.

The other day I was outside pulling some khaki weed, just to be doing something since the sun was up. She came out. Talked earnestly in the way she does now, using her small group of remembered words, and went back inside. I had no idea what she wanted. I finished up a few minutes later and went to the house. When I walked in I knew why she came out. Dinner was ready. A Tim Burton nightmare dinner. Two plates, neatly arranged with a fork beside each. On each plate was a microwaved bread sandwich, covered in syrup. The plate was full. A salad bowl sat to the right with a graham cracker in it. An investigation showed the sandwich was nothing but mayonnaise.

In a perfect world I would have reacted as if a six-year-old had prepared the dinner. Graciously. *Thanks, that's sweet of you to fix dinner, how kind*, I would have said, as I swept the contents into the disposal, counting it as a cute act on the upward tick of the Bell curve of life. But, no, taken by surprise, and knowing we were on the other side of the mountain, my tired, simian brain blew up. I'm pretty sure she had no idea why I was ranting around as I cleaned, but there I was making a perfect fool of myself. Ticked off in large part, I suppose, because one of the best cooks I'd ever known was reduced to this, and I had no one's heart to rip out in revenge except my own. When I finished cleaning, I took her out to dinner, and she was happy.

A Moment of Joy

Monday, November 5, 2018

In the long dark slog through the desolation of my wife's illness there's increasingly little light to break the darkness. What light that does come is welcome, however, and when I know it's coming, cherished. A dinner with friends, a visit by family, a trip to a sporting event, live music. They all serve to break the spell and lighten the mood. They give me a chance to anticipate something good.

In May of last year our long-time friends gifted me with a chance to sing and play on stage at their house concert as an opener for their neighbors, the Flying A's. It was a nice evening. They did it again this past weekend, when they asked me to open for Walt and Tina Wilkins. It's a gracious thing for someone to do that for you, offer you a spot on their stage out of consideration and love, friend and musicians alike. You have to believe there will be rewards for people like that.

As for myself, the preparation was nearly as important as the event. Thinking about the songs. Practicing. Wondering how they would be received. Hoping for the best. Using it all as stepping stones across the wasteland. Imagining I was as cool as Dave Grohl while knowing it was more likely I was a dim shadow of a cast member of the Lawrence Welk show. Still, it was something to anticipate, and savor as it happened, and given that I met my wife through music it felt good to play it and know there were still songs in my heart, the last refuge of the light.

At First Glance

Tuesday, November 6, 2018

There are moments when everything seems normal. A glance at my wife sitting in her chair playing on her iPad. A glimpse of her walking around the gardens looking at the plants. The touch of her hand as we take a stroll. Her smile when she sees me enter the room. But the pantry is locked, as is the refrigerator, and the microwave is unplugged, and the stove turned off at the breaker, because all is far from normal. As the synapses fail, words like "hot" no longer mean anything, instructions are useless, and the only thing she can do safely in the kitchen is make single cups of coffee.

I've installed one camera to monitor her as she sleeps, and another so that I can watch her as she moves about the front room. There's incontinence and the nearly daily washing of sheets, help with bathing, and making sure the clothes are clean. Hardly onerous chores. I helped raise three kids. They all wet their pants, and needed help with bathing, and getting the right clothes on. It's just that I never expected to do it for their mother. She'd probably be appalled I was sharing this, but life is messy, and there are lots of unpleasant facts that shouldn't be ignored.

After all, it seems a shame to go on a journey and not tell anyone what you saw, because passing along information may be helpful for someone preparing for or enduring the same trip. My biggest tip is to get a guide. I have a nice counselor who holds my emotional hand and gives advice, and keeps repeating that I need to be sure and live my life and not let myself get consumed in the caregiving. I nod in understanding, except my life includes this woman, so that's a conundrum. I guess the best anyone can do is keep trying, and that I shall do.

A Bedtime Story

Wednesday, November 7, 2018

We have a comfortable couch. I know because I sleep on it at night. It sits just outside our bedroom door and it allows me to know if my wife gets up during the night. If I sleep in our king bed, it's too easy to get into a really deep sleep and miss her departure. It's sort of the same mindset we had when the kids were young. There were no monitors so we became light sleepers and sensitive to noise.

At the moment she's slumbering, which is good, but then again she didn't get to bed until midnight. So, this is about right. Her circadian rhythm is playing avant-garde jazz with lots of time changes. Unfortunately, I'm still plodding along at 4/4. If you prefer a computer analogy, her sleep setting is choosing random numbers, and there's no way to find the settings tab to adjust it, even if you Google it all night long.

The nighttime wandering wasn't that bad before, but now the cross-wiring around how things work is causing problems. She knows the sense of things but not the details. This is especially problematic with microwaves and toaster ovens. So, she needs watching, and watching she gets, even if it means sleeping on the couch. I'm glad we got rid of the leather one. It was too cold and stiff for good sleeping.

Part 3: Facing the Inevitable

Dementia is a degenerative disease. The brain, the most beautiful organ in the body, fails slowly over time. The act of helping a person suffering with this failure is relentless. Most of us are ill-prepared for the job. In some ways, it resembles a swimmer coming to the rescue. If you know what you're doing, it is possible to save someone and return successfully to shore. If not, you are just as likely to drown as the one being rescued.

This is why caregivers are constantly reminded to seek help for their own mental and physical wellbeing. I concur. Get counseling. Get in-home help. As a society, we're groomed to applaud the sufferer, the one giving all to help another. But, as my counselor once told me, most times this simply leads to the death of two people rather than just one.

I kept up as long as I could because I wanted her to stay home. I was fortunate. We had insurance, and I was able to buy help. A lady came daily to the house. But eventually, even that proved to be too little. And since I had the option to provide her with 24/7 care it seemed a prudent thing to do. I did it. The psychological ramifications were acute. I felt guilty, as though I was abandoning her. I continued going to counseling, but the guilty feelings never let up.

Moving on Down the Road

Thursday, November 8, 2018

Managing the medical care of a loved one who is unable to offer input into the care is difficult. Then there's the delicate balance of doing what is best for the patient while considering the needs of the caregiver. I'm walking that tightrope. Luckily, I have a coterie of doctors, family and friends who act as a long balancing pole to help keep me safe on the wire. It's comforting.

I say this because on the morrow my wife will go to a memory care facility, where the 24-hours-a-day care is unrelenting. It's a small place, just down the road toward Fredericksburg. There are 16 beds, a big yard beneath large oaks, and a caring staff. She has gone there on several occasions for short breaks, and she appears to be comfortable in the surroundings. I have no idea as to the duration. It may be, with rest and reflection, I can find a way to bring her home, or it may be this is just how our world ends.

I've gone back and forth between feeling like a Victorian earl squirreling his wife away in an asylum to feeling as though I've just rented a long-term storage unit for humans. Everyone, from my counselor to our doctors to our friends and my children say otherwise. They tell me this is good for both of us. I guess it's nice they have the perspective of distance, and my rational mind agrees with them, and I'd give a friend the same advice. But the guilt is there, driven by the idea that while I signed up for better or for worse, somehow I'm running from the worse. I don't think that's the case, but the mind can play tricks. I guess that's why they tell you to get plenty of sleep. Deep breath. Here's to the future, such as it is.

The Name of the Game

Tuesday, November 13, 2018

Brought in the plants, emptied the exposed water pipes and got ready for a freeze. Did most of the work in a light drizzle. It felt good shutting things down in anticipation of winter. The freeze is forecast for tonight, but the cold is definitely already here along with a breeze. The combination is designed to keep me inside, and inside I shall stay.

I watched the wind blow the yellow bells yesterday. They looked as though they wanted to run away, get inside where it was warm along with the geraniums and the ficus, but their feet are stuck in the mud and escape is hopeless. I felt bad for them. They spent all summer growing tall to bloom in the fall and they get repaid with a freeze designed to kill flowers and leaves. It seems ungrateful, but there's nothing I can do.

I did take care of the cats. Brought down the old kennels, covered them up and put blankets in them, with a warming light. They all got inside and kept one another warm. It reminded me of the days when my bride and I lived in homes with gas heaters. They'd be shut off at night and we'd snuggle down under the quilts and keep one another warm as well. Those were the days of youth, filled with promise. Gone now. Replaced by age and disease and the inexplicable. Endurance is the name of the game these days as we prepare to embrace winter.

Way Down Yonder

Thursday, November 15, 2018

It's another frosty mornin'. I guess the cold is taking a second crack at anything that survived the night before. It's looking fairly wilted around here. Grass, vines, and flowering plants have all succumbed. The hearty ones will put their energies into feeding their roots. The rest will pass into the realm of departed vegetation.

The wild grape vines were quick to give up their leaves. They went from vibrant green to brown in an instant. The bind weed that had climbed into the crown of the flame leaf sumac is likewise done, a dark lump hanging lifeless in the leaves. It will be easy to trace it back to the roots and pull it up. The morning glories are also gone for the season. There are still blooms on the scarlet sage, but its leaves are done and there will be nothing but bare branches soon enough, probably after the first good breeze.

I guess it's fitting all this happens four days after my wife goes into memory care. The bloom is off the rose as they say, although her favorite rose bush, tucked behind the orchid tree at the east end of the house, is enduring fairly well. Still, it seems a little bare around here, less bright, surrounded by fading pictures with only the sound of the wind against the windows to break the silence. I've been alone before and will be again, but this feels different. I guess it's up to me to make something of it.

And Now This

Saturday, November 17, 2018

Observation. The world closes in around me at night. In the light, there's the input of the world. In the dark, there's just me. A lamp may illuminate the room, but it's only one place in the entire house, in the town, in the state, in the country. I sit in my chair, surrounded by empty chairs and it's an odd feeling because always before there was another person in the room, helping to keep the darkness at bay. That's changed.

I'm at peace with the change, and this is not a cry for help. It's only an observation. A feeling catalogued along the journey. I'm here; she's there. Circumstances dictate the actions. Choices have been made. It's that time after a surgery when everything hurts, and they tell you to walk and you walk and there's pain and then eventually it's gone. That will come. There will be a scar for sure, but at this stage in my life, what's another scar. At least the world continues to turn, and I'm here to notice.

It made the turn toward light this morning. I was on the porch, and the little black kitten said hello. Not in so many words, but with just a look. I like that little black cat. My son made a brief appearance last night to tell me he'd clean out the workroom as requested, and a friend called to talk a little business and enquire as to my wellbeing, and a text message arrived to schedule a lunch. Life goes on, and on, and on, and on.

Little Things

Monday, November 19, 2018

I'm a good Texan in winter. When a hard freeze beckons, I know to bring in the plants, shelter the animals, and drain exposed water lines. When the freeze threatened last week, I did just that. There was only one problem. When I drained the lines on our well, I neglected the lowest point in the line. The water and the cold proved its supremacy by creating ice and blowing apart the PVC.

I fixed it this weekend, a complicated arrangement of joints and tees with a ball valve at the end. Lots of cutting and primer and cement. It took on aspects of a military operation. A board to lay out the parts, the miter saw to cut the pipe, a pipe wrench to tighten it up. A big dollop of patience as I knew haste would indeed make waste. When it was all put together I waited overnight to pressure it up. Still, there was a leak around the faucets. A quick turn, however, and no more leak. I was back in business.

I'm no stranger to fixing my broken bits. From septic tanks, to toilets, to water wells, to cars. I've learned how to dive in and get it done. Necessity, mostly. Lack of funds to pay others to do it. I realized a long while back, however, that something else was at play. Fixing the broken thing was empowering. When Life dealt its insults, I'd fix it. I could fight against the chaos in my little corner of the universe, and win. And even when something's brokenness is beyond my ability to repair, as with my wife's illness, I can still do my best to beat back the tide and refuse to surrender. So, let it freeze. I know what to do, until I can't, but that's one battle no one wins. And I'll cross that bridge when I come to it.

The Fractal Dimension

Thursday, November 29, 2018

I opened a book this morning, and there was a coaster I thought I'd lost. Why was the coaster there? Probably because it had been easier to grab the coaster from the table than to get up and search for a better bookmark. Then the book itself got swept up into the general maelstrom of life until I needed it this morning to illustrate a point. And oddly enough the coaster was at precisely the page I needed. Now there's some serendipity for you.

So, here goes. I think we all have little holes in our souls or tears in our hearts brought on by the wear and tear of daily life. Disappointments, loss, and failure all contribute to the gouging and the cutting. How do we survive? My guess: we keep moving. We fill our sails with the breath of life, and those little holes scarcely impede our moving forward. The example I wanted was a Sierpinsky carpet. In this carpet of the mathematician's imagination, you can remove an infinite amount of volume from a finite space.

This all came about as I sat with a group of friends last night listening to music. I realized, as I looked around the room, that almost everyone there probably had borne some sort of trial or tribulation, tearing little holes in their souls. Yet, they were smiling and laughing and reaching out to help one another even without knowing it. It made me think that perhaps we are all part of one sail, one soul, and one heart; little strands reaching out to grasp a neighboring strand in times of trouble. Existing even in the face of what might seem insurmountable loss. Working around the inevitable holes, letting the wind blow through, yet keeping us moving. A paradox, for sure. But proof that we're not alone and that mathematicians aren't crazy.

A Warm Winter's Day

Friday, November 30, 2018

The morning greeted me with a Gulf breeze full of moisture and warmth. We're in that cycle where we get to explain to people from the North why we like to live in Texas: because you can still play golf in December and January since the biting cold comes in two- and three-day increments. You get to wear jackets, and then take them off to put on shorts and it's all lovely and cool. (Of course, I still have a no linen or shorts policy after Labor Day, but I'm old fashioned.)

There's a new nursery in Blanco where I'm going later this morning to pick up a few plants. Actually, it's an old nursery with new owners. I had a nice chat with the lady who runs it yesterday as I killed time waiting for a dental appointment. I'm going to get a prostrate rosemary plant to replace the one I lost, and a few pansies for winter color. I may also pick up some small Gulf muhly's. It depends on how much I want to stress the budget.

I also need to fix a swinging gate and I'll probably do that on Saturday. My will to work is strengthening, which is good. For the last several weeks I've mainly walked around thinking, I should fix that. The time has come. Weird how that works. Desire and opportunity meet on a warmish Friday in November. I wish they could get together more quickly, because it seems as though I have a much longer list of things to do than of things I've done. Although maybe it's a case of having once done them they leave my mind. I'll go with that. Surely I've accomplished something in all these years.

In the Spirit

Monday, December 10, 2018

The stockings are now hung by the chimney with care. My daughter and her husband made the trip in this weekend from Houston to help with the chore. I did the outside decorations as I always did, by myself, my usual role in the unfolding of the Christmas spirit at our house. But my wife ruled the inside world. I helped, but it was her place to putter and decorate. That ended last year, as she seemed blissfully unaware of the holiday. I took on the new unaccustomed role and did the best I could. But it seemed almost joyless, and I knew I'd need help this year.

My daughter offered, and I accepted. They arrived on Friday night. We visited late into the evening, looked at old pictures and talked about her mother. The next morning I fixed a big breakfast and then we got started. We hauled boxes and boxes of ornaments and decorations down from the attic. It's amazing what you collect over 48 years. We discussed where things went. Some I knew, but others were more mysterious because we were missing the chief decorator. In the end, we got it all up and this year the house is decorated to a fare thee well. It feels nice and all-encompassing, full of the spirit of the missing wife. We finished the day with a nice meal around the old table that we've had since the first time we hosted a family dinner in 1986.

On Sunday, our son joined us as we bundled up and went to visit the missing mother and wife. The kids tidied up their mother's room, hung a few extra pictures, and cried at random moments. They talked with her friends who wandered in and out of her room. They walked around the courtyard and sat outside in the sun and had a lovely visit. It ended when lunch was served, and their mother's focus shifted to the meal at hand. My daughter drove back to the house with her brother. I imagine the mood was somber, but they're good kids and I've tried to keep them in the loop, and I expect they'll find ways to help one another just as they've helped me. Next up is Christmas its own self. Then I'll have all my children in the house. Joy to the world.

Joseph and the Duck

Wednesday, December 12, 2018

We have a ceramic nativity scene which, if memory serves, was created by my wife. The details, of course, are lost to the mists of time because my wife loved doing crafts and I got totally used to things just showing up. We displayed it each Christmas until several years back when she decided, for some reason, that we no longer had space. It stayed in its box locked in the attic until this year, when my daughter was here to help with the decorating.

Everything was fair game, and we were going all in. We both liked the Nativity set and felt it needed re-exposure. Down it came to be unboxed. Almost immediately, we noticed two things: Joseph had lost his head; and there was a ceramic duck. I have no idea when Joseph lost his head. It most likely happened when my wife was putting up things after Christmas and may explain why it stopped being brought out. My quick-witted daughter fixed Joseph by putting a nut on his shoulders, and since he was in the shadows of the manger that worked fine.

The duck was something else entirely. First, there is no mention of a duck at the Nativity. Second, as a ceramic piece goes, it's as tall as a kneeling Wiseman, which if it was scaled up would make it about an eight-foot-tall duck in the real world. We talked about taking it out, but in the end, we thought it was a good reminder of her mother and my wife and that it should stay. It seemed emblematic of the odd connections my wife's disease probably had started making even before we knew they were being made. It's the only explanation we have as to why it was wrapped up with the Nativity set. As explanations go, it's as good as any and I'm fairly certain the baby Jesus wouldn't have minded a really tall duck coming to see what's up and staying to say hello.

'Tis the Season 2

Monday, December 17, 2018

I'm nearly finished with my Christmas shopping. Almost all of it happened online with packages arriving to be stacked on the floor of my office for wrapping. In previous years, my wife would have handled all of that with me taking care of certain delegated purchases. The gifts would have been wrapped by now and sitting under the tree awaiting distribution. She would have known to the dollar how much was spent on each child or person. She kept the numbers and the gifts in her head with a stack of receipts to back it up.

I have a spreadsheet. I refined it a bit this year, when I decided I didn't want to see anyone's gift list ahead of time. I was going to give them all things I thought they'd like. There will probably be a few disappointed faces, but our kids are good about being grateful for the act of giving, and take odd presents with a practiced aplomb, expressing gratitude to the giver, finding pleasure in the act of receiving a gift. Although, there is the famous story of the time my grandson received a nutcracker. His youthful response has entered family legend.

I took up the shopping chore last year, when I realized my wife had no idea Christmas was coming. It was even difficult to get her to go Christmas shopping. My daughter tried, but to no avail. On Christmas Day we had to coach her when it came time to open her presents. It's an odd feeling to watch someone who used to take such delight in the holiday no longer know that the holiday is here. It sucks a lot of the joy out of the season. But this past weekend, when I donned a seldom-worn suit, I found a funeral memento from a service I'd attended in January for the daughter of a friend who died last Christmas Day. It gave me pause. At least, I can still visit my wife. My friend has to go to a cemetery to visit her daughter.

As Time Goes By

Friday, December 21, 2018

I had some technology excitement last night. Earlier in the day, I went to visit my bride at the memory care center. I did the usual, tidied up, brought in a new picture, replaced an old one, sat with her, and charged up her iPad. That's when things got interesting. That evening I started getting text messages from friends telling me that she was actively sending out "friend" requests on Facebook. My first thought was that her account had been hacked; that was their first thought as well. I checked her account, however, and that wasn't the case. She was really doing it.

The "friending" action manifested one of the insidious elements of her illness. Actions can be remembered but there's no language to give them context. She does things without understanding why. This could create the appearance of cognition, but it's a false positive. This time, she even posted something: the single word, "Past." I spent a while changing various security settings to limit her exposure to nefarious elements, but I knew most of the folks that were becoming her friends and those I didn't know I could identify by seeing mutual friends. They were classmates and members of her organizations.

At some point I might delete the app from her device, but for now I think I can stay on top of it. I'll be a silent hand, letting her be herself as much as she can be in the current circumstances. Of course, our mutual friends will be there as well. That's why I got the text messages last night. It reminded me of life in Alvin years ago when we'd get calls from friends and neighbors who saw our children doing something they thought was questionable. I always appreciated the concern as I do in this case. Of course, there won't be any growing up, no chance later to share memories during a holiday or dinner. She's not making new synapses, she's losing them. And that, Facebook, is what's on my mind.

The Holiday

Thursday, December 27, 2018

There was a joyful noise in the house this Christmas. The children and their children gathered, and for several bright moments laughter and happy chatter filled the air. We assembled around the tree, exchanged presents, wore our new clothes, played with games, smelled candles and bath salts, and just generally enjoyed one another's company. We slept on couches and on floors and in beds, ate large collective breakfasts, and shared lunches of left-overs, leavened with plenty of sweets because, hey, it's Christmas.

On several occasions we all bundled up and made the trip down the road to visit the mother and wife. She was happy to see everyone and held hands and touched faces and pointed at pictures to assure people, as best she could, she knew who they were, although we weren't sure she knew the grandchildren, who are well past their baby days and into their form-changing years. There was little catching up to do. We're down to the tactile now, a universe of soft touches and soothing tones, everyone alone with their thoughts, such as they are.

At some point in the coming weeks I'll begin disassembling the Christmas decorations, stacking and storing them and returning the house to a more level, less festive appearance. Anything less, and I might begin to resemble Miss Haversham hanging on to the past with a death grip, except I'd exchange a moldy wedding cake for a dusty Christmas tree. We can't have that. I will take my time, however, because I want to repackage some of the goodies for better storage, which will give me the chance to linger, ever so surreptitiously, with the past, or what's left of it, before I return it to the attic.

114

It's In the Cards

Friday, December 28, 2018

Our address book is blue, covered in gold moons and stars. It's well worn. In it you can find friends and family carefully annotated over the years with changes in addresses and phone numbers. I used it, but less so as phones got better, and felt it was antiquarian. But last year, when I took up the duty of writing Christmas cards I discovered its value. There, along the edges of each address was a wavering line of two-digit numbers indicating who got a card that year.

I followed along, adding 2017 and then 2018. But as I received cards this year I began to realize, while I may have been following the rules of the cards, I was missing the spirit. My wife fretted over their purchase and took days to sign and send them. Likewise, our friends, apparently. It really struck me this year, for the first time, how much attention to detail they contained. There were personal notes, letters, and even a hand-painted card from my cousin. I have no idea why the dedication never registered before. Male pattern blindness, I guess; the inability to see the obvious. I was allocating one day for the chore and, in my typical industrial fashion, was trying to figure out how to use my printer to do the addressing. That would have been a cosmic mistake.

Nope. The Christmas card tradition was another little thing in the myriad of little things my wife did to maintain and foster relationships. It was done with attention to detail and with an eye toward the message, which was simple: I'm thinking of you. It's why she still has friends she sees on a regular basis from her days as a first-grader. Nice role model. It's one more reason why I'm happy she took a shine to me, and with that in mind, I'm already thinking about next year's cards.

A Springtime Thought

Monday, December 31, 2018

I never took my wife to Paris in the spring or any other time. She wanted to go, but it never happened. We went to London, Amsterdam, Zurich, and Frankfurt. We drove through the Swiss Alps, ate lunch in Austria, and she took a boat ride on the Rhine. We spent a week in Hawaii, stood beside the Christmas tree in Rockefeller Center, boated beneath Niagara Falls, and walked on the beach at La Jolla. But it's too late for Paris. It's even too late to apologize. She wouldn't know what I was talking about.

Of course, it's also unlikely she remembers any of those things we did. So, even if we'd gone to Paris there'd be nothing there and no way to talk about it. Our visits are mostly confined to hand-holding, kisses on the cheek, and walks beneath the big oaks. She remembers the kids and most of our friends when she sees them. There are joyful looks, faces held, and even a kiss. But then the visit becomes mostly silent and slightly awkward. I guess if there's an upside, it also means she's forgotten anything I did to hurt her, a mean word, a strong look, forgetting an anniversary. The slate is being wiped clean, more or less.

The one consolation I have is that since she always seems happy to see me, it implies maybe I was right more than I was wrong, at least in the essence of things. Hard to believe, however, that that's the distillation of 48 years of marriage. But you take what you can get, because the deal was for better or worse, and I've always been a fan of finding silver linings. Still, I wish we'd done Paris. She would have liked that.

One More for the Pile

Friday, January 4, 2019

It's strange how time seems to slow when it gets cold. Perhaps that's because it narrows my range of options, forcing me inside to smaller ground. I can see why bears hibernate. Yesterday was a slow day. I read, paid bills, cleaned the bathroom, washed a few towels and dishcloths and hung them on the line to dry. I like the clothes hanging bit. As a child it was always one of my jobs. Hang'em, take'em down, fold'em.

Yesterday, I nearly forgot them on the line, however, and when I retrieved them, the evening dew was starting to settle, and they felt a little damp. Although sometimes it's hard to discern the difference between dampness and cold. At the moment, they're still in the basket waiting for me to finish the job and fold them. My mother would not be happy. If there was a bit of moisture, it's probably gone by now after a night in the artificial heat of my American house.

Speaking of dishcloths, one of the things I've noticed in my semi-wifeless state is the little oddities of her approach to the tiny cleaning tool. We have a drawer with a wide variety of little dish cleaning squares. Some are crocheted and to my untrained eye look like pot holders, but I know we washed with them. So, the question for me is, was that intentional, or a first indication of disappearing neurons? I'm not real sure it matters, because it's not like anyone talks about the five warning signs your wife's brain is disappearing. I just wish I hadn't missed that moment of engagement to hear her take on the issue. Just another regret to go with all the others.

One for the Team

Saturday, January 12, 2019

We have a squeegee in our shower. It's there to clean the water off the glass when the shower is done to stop the calcium build-up. It was my wife's idea. And she would always check after I took a shower to see if I cleaned the glass. It was one of those intersections of male working life and female home life that often occur. I had no idea cleaning calcium off the glass was an onerous task, having never done it, but my wife did and she was all-in on preventive maintenance.

I have no idea where she picked up the tip. All I know is that I sensed, as I assume most husbands do, that this was an issue that brooked little discussion. There was a squeegee and it was to be used. I used it. After she went in to the memory care facility, I showered and left without wiping the glass, feeling I could probably dispense with this proscribed activity. But it didn't take long for the guilt to set in, and I went back to doing as I was asked, because she was right and why not take a moment to save yourself a lot of hard work later on down the line.

Besides, it gives me a sense of normalcy, which is a little hard to come by these days as I trundle around in an empty house, keeping it all clean and neat because that's how she liked it. I always tried to keep it neat when she went off to visit relatives or spend a weekend with her Ya-Ya's (close girlfriends). I didn't want her to come home to a messy house and think I was a slob, even though she knew better. I wanted her glad to be home, and I really wish I could once again hear the sound of her car coming up the drive.

118

Treasures, Wednesday

January 16, 2019

I am on a journey through the cabinets. We have lots of them, in the kitchen, in the utility room, and all around the house. Places for things. So far my travels have revealed many mysterious wonders, things long forgotten and some thought lost. I discovered a Dust Devil, handy for vacuuming the inside of my car. I found a cache of incense. Best of all, I found a tiny ceramic bowl full of keys. Several of the keys unlocked the doors to my workroom. I'd been looking for the only known member of that key family for quite some time, and thought it lost. It is, but its siblings are now found. Rejoice.

There is an entire shelf dedicated to candle holders. I recognized one of them as a Christmas present to my wife from years past. I was glad to see it. I may bring it out and set a large candle on it once again. There were several others of indeterminate origins; most likely they were items once needed and bought to brighten the house. My wife always tinkered with the look of our abode much to my benefit and pleasure. A bit of color here, a light there. The table tops and walls always shifted with her vision.

It was one of those lucky things that happens when two lives intertwine and the presence of each radiates throughout the house to the benefit and pleasure of both. I've been doing my best to recreate her seasonal visions, but as I've discovered in my journey through the cabinets, I was only privy to the external manifestations of her thoughts. The memories of where things were kept and her ideas for using them are locked away or lost with her decline. The harmony of the house is missing a voice, and only the echoes linger in the rooms.

How It Goes

Friday, February 8, 2019

Winter has reappeared. Terrific. I like the February cold. And the darkness. And moroseness. It's the time of year when I prepare for spring. I need quiet. I'm about two-thirds of the way along in the cleanout of the back porch garden. As I go, I'm also clearing the path. The dirt is soft and the weeds come up easily and the designated survivors seem perky and fresh and glad to be free of the competition. They probably feel as though the noisy loud neighbors that moved in over the summer have suddenly disappeared.

There's still a ways to go, however. The bed close to the porch and the path beside it are only two components of the little back porch garden complex. The faux creek bed also needs cleaning. I plan on lifting all the rocks and putting down new weed shield material. It came to me this morning how to accomplish the task and it involves working it in sections rather than trying to move all the rocks at once. I didn't yell *eureka*, but I felt like it.

I think that if my wife was still at home and able to communicate, we would have come up with a plan a lot sooner. I miss having that sort of interaction. I used to work with a man who believed in what he called "The Bigger Brain." It was something that resulted from a team of people working together. It's a version of two heads are better than one. That's how it was for us. Now, I'm left to plot and plan on my own, and it's difficult to chart a course when you've only got one oar in the water.

The Spice of Life

Thursday, March 14, 2019

I took my bride for a ride. Date night redux. Although, it was a lot less romantic than dinner and a movie. We went to do blood work and followed it up with breakfast at a local restaurant. We passed the meal in silence, because her language skills are gone. Still, it was a good first step for her to go out since she relocated to the memory care facility. She returned "home" without complaint, and we have another date scheduled for tomorrow. She doesn't know this, however, because, well, language.

The next outing will be longer. It involves a trip to see our cardiologist. He lets us schedule our appointments together. He's a nice man who is retiring in June; that's sad and another story all together. If all goes according to plan, the appointments will last long enough that we should be able to stop for an early dinner. That actually works well, because she normally eats at around five o'clock. We can lollygag on our way back to her place and have a nice afternoon together.

Other outings are in the plans, now that the first went so well. I can start taking her to lunch, or we can go shopping, or we can just ride around in the car. Reminds me a bit of our courting days, doing nothing in particular, just hanging out. It's certainly good for me, because I'll have something to anticipate and it will be good for her because it will add variety to her days and she's still happy to see me when I come by. Ultimately, these little trips will be the long coda of our *pas de deux*, a final silent parade across the stage as we end our dance together.

No Sugar

Saturday, March 16, 2019

The hard part of writing about life with dementia is the tendency to avoid the difficult bits. But that really seems to be the core of the experience. It's all mind-bendingly difficult. Every time a new experience arrives there's another adjustment to make, another wrap of the head around a problem I never imagined would come my way. Yet, here it comes, boldly expecting me to deal with it, and this is where it gets tricky.

The new experiences are mostly surprises, and while some surprises elicit joy and happiness (think Christmas or birthdays), in this case they usually startle and can cause loud, angry noises. Take having your car door opened at 70 miles per hour to discard a piece of stray hair. My wife used to roll down her window to do that and open the door when we stopped. Yesterday, she went straight to the door. Luckily, there was a wide spot to stop and get things buttoned back up. But the old autonomic nervous system went into hyperdrive and I yelled. I've spent a lifetime trying to wipe that approach from my repertoire of responses, but there it was, bold and ugly.

The easy thing would be to gloss over it and talk about our trip to the doctor yesterday as if it was a journey into the Hundred Acre Wood. But that's fiction and this is real life, with bladders gone wonky, with boundaries and controls stripped away, and no way to communicate except through looks and gestures. The long afternoon was spent explaining the unexplainable to one unable to comprehend anything. It wore away my equanimity in a surprisingly rapid fashion, and there I was: the man I've tried desperately to cast aside. It was a disappointing outcome.

One of These Days

Tuesday, March 19, 2019

It's odd the things I miss. Take letter openers. It was actually an accoutrement to my desk along with a paperweight back in the days when I sold books for a living. Both are probably in a box somewhere in the attic. I don't miss the paperweight, but the letter opener sure would come in handy. I may have to mount a search party to see if I can find it. I'm pretty sure the kitchen knives I'm using aren't the ideal tool for the job, although they are sharp, and the letters open quickly. It would just be nice to have a purpose-built device close at hand.

Of course, there's every possibility that wanting that letter opener is just an old man reaching back into his past when everything was right, more or less, with the world. The kids were young, the wife healthy, and we were having a good time. Plus, as jobs go, selling books all over the world was a fine gig especially for an English Major. There was plenty of travel, the authors were interesting, the booksellers nice, and most of my compatriots were smart, intelligent people. There were exceptions, of course, but there always are. In the long run, I'll probably just let the letter opener be. It's done its time and deserves a rest.

As for me, I'll muddle along with my memories and continue trying to make new ones. Although, it does occur to me that at some point I'll do something and there won't be enough time left for it to become a memory. That's a weird thought. I wonder how you classify that? I guess it's like a last paragraph in a book. It just ends, and you're none the wiser. At that point you become a memory for someone else, until, poof, you're just a picture in a photo album and no one knows your name.

One Step Over the Line

Wednesday, March 20, 2019

Oh, joy. The old left-side sciatic nerve is irritated with me. Apparently, lifting bags of hardwood mulch from the trunk of my car is different than sliding them out of the bed of my pickup. It seems as though I should have known that. But, no. My mind is making promises my body can't keep. Now the bill is due. After three days of no sleep, because my leg hurt like hell while lying in bed, I finally went to the doctor who poked around, nodded gravely, and then gave me a muscle relaxer, a steroid, and some stretching exercises.

I was relieved to hear it wasn't an embolism, which is something folks my age can suffer, but upset to realize I'd mismanaged my back. It's an old adversary. Apparently, however, rather than a peace treaty, we simply signed an armistice and my back, led by the duplicitous nerve, decided to test the boundaries. Fine. I think my mind has decided that if I'm going to put my wife in a memory care facility I need to experience a little physical discomfort to go along with the mental anguish. I'm two colds, a busted-up finger, a wrecked car, and an achy back into my punishment this year. Hardly the travails of Job, but, what is?

The common wisdom says I shouldn't punish myself, but that's the common wisdom, and the mind, when you still have one, is a tricky thing. There's probably a default switch somewhere that says, "if she's gone, you're gone," hardwired from the days when you needed two people to kill the mastodon or else you went hungry. Of course, there's nothing like being your own doctor or psychologist. It's roughly equivalent to being your own financial advisor, which is how you end up owing your soul to the company store. So, I'm off to find professional help, before I drive myself off a cliff believing I can fly. It seems the prudent thing to do.

When the Teardrops Fall

Thursday, March 21, 2019

It's a blessed feeling to wake from a good night's sleep when the previous several nights had been broken by intense pain for which there was little relief. It happened to me this morning. As my mind surged back into consciousness, the first thing I did was inventory the nerves in my leg that just yesterday felt red-hot and fiery. There was a dull ache, but nothing resembling the fierce flames of the days before. A quick check of the clock showed I'd been abed for about seven hours. It was one of those modern-day miracles.

A single day of a drug regimen, including a muscle relaxer and a steroid, and my pain was banished to a distant, lightly throbbing memory. By the time the program is complete, I should be back to something approaching normal. My mind will check the wounded areas once in a while to make sure all is well, but after a bit, we'll go on about our business. All will be right with the world. I was happy, and I don't know why, but also I found myself wondering how those afflicted with chronic pain deal with it.

My three days of torture nearly brought me to tears, but I was sure there would be relief in the end. It came. But those with conditions resisting treatment have to endure their agony on a daily basis with only modest relief. And the loved ones supporting them have to suffer as well, watching their young one or a spouse be tortured as bodies fail or refuse to work. I wish I could lay hands on all of them and provide the same relief I just received, but that's a grandiose wish sure to fail. Maybe just thinking about them helps in some mysterious way. It's worth a try. So, that's what I'll do today as I take my medicines and heal. I'll think about the sick and wounded who will get no such easy relief.

To Have and to Hold

Sunday, March 23, 2019

Another thing I miss with my wife in memory care—touch. A hug, a random squeeze of the shoulder, a hand to hold while drifting off to sleep. There were probably more instances because it's hard, over the course of a day, to totally avoid contact, and I think they're too innumerable, and constant, to catalog. It's probably why two humans live together, or any other animal for that matter. Contact, the physical affirmation of not being alone.

I was reminded of this when I got a good massage yesterday. There were knots and sore spots in all the places where my body has decided to tense up and store my anxiety and stress. It felt good to have them kneaded into submission, although it will take more than one session to banish them. Still, it was a good start. And it probably wasn't as bad as it could have been, because I have friends and family who all like to hug and no greeting is complete without one, and since I see them on a fairly regular basis, I've been hugged plenty.

Still, there's always a bit of left-over stress and it needs to go somewhere, so random muscles pick up the slack. This is where the masseuse comes in handy. She knows where the demons live and can rouse them with a touch and help them get a move on. After that it's up to me to keep things in action, a stretch here, a movement there, to do the things that keep the body from becoming an immobilized mass of muscle and gristle. You take all this for granted when you're young; you're flexible in spite of yourself. Age, though. That tells the tale. Use it or lose it. Which brings to mind the advice that when you find yourself in hell, keep moving, it's the only way out.

TV Time, Friday

March 29, 2019

A while back I bought some cameras to help monitor my wife's whereabouts on the property. She wasn't allowed to drive, but she could walk and she'd often head down to the corner store unannounced. That trip involved crossing five lanes of Highway 290 on foot. Hardly the safest proposition. The cameras worked okay, and I hired some help, but eventually it all proved redundant when she went into memory care and I hardly needed to keep track of the activity on my suburban estate to that level.

Then I discovered a nicely dug burrow beneath a lantana in the back yard and I thought it would be fun to see what was up. An armadillo is what, along with two neighborhood cats and a raccoon with a kit. It seems the burrow is right by a hole in our fence and the nightlife uses it as a thoroughfare. The cats and the raccoons are coming to check the food supply. I feed our cats in the dog run. I usually take the food in at night, but sometimes forget. The neighbors know this and come 'round just to visit and have a snack if one's available.

It's oddly satisfying to watch the comings and goings of the animal kingdom at night. When I get the notification on my phone it's a bit like seeing the cork bob when I used to fish. Of course, I'm not going to reel anything in except a picture, and the show is usually short, but they're my critters and they're fun to watch, and maybe one day if they do something especially entertaining I'll share it. In the meantime, I'm just going to be an easily entertained old man and let it go at that.

In the Trees

Friday, March 29, 2019

A while back my youngest son, the arborist, gifted his mother with Spanish moss. It might seem a strange gift to some, but the intent was pure. Draped in our big oaks, he wanted to help her recall the trees of her youth in South Louisiana. Unfortunately, her disease left her unable to understand the intent and enjoy its meaning. She started picking at the new visitors trying to clean her trees. We deflected her and, ultimately, she lost interest.

The moss endured, however, and now hangs, blowing in the wind like fragments of wispy memories, reminding us, instead of her, of what was lost. I'm good with that. I like moss-covered trees because lots of her South Louisiana days were mine as well. When we married her multitudinous family subsumed me and made it their goal to ensure I knew I was now part of the clan. We hunted ducks, spent time at the beach, fried fish, ate gumbo, drank beer and just generally attacked life with gusto. It was fun. The aunts and uncles of her youth are now mostly gone, but lots of the cousins are still there. One of them even owns property just south of town up in the hills behind Miller Creek. Talk about a small world.

My wife, a dogged genealogist because of the DAR, knew the ins and outs of her family through all the generations, up to and including the present. She wrote, she visited, she talked to them. That's all past, now; the branches of those memories are broken and strewn about. But I'm trying to pick up the slack because I know they loved my wife and she them and me as well. They were her refuge through troubled times and a constant she could count on. When it gets right down to it and she's no longer able, it's up to us to keep her memories alive by sharing them with one another as best we can. Given all she did for us, it seems only fair.

Endearing Young Charms

Saturday, May 4, 2019

I got the call. There's been a fall. She's fine. She cracked a tooth. Well, broke it. Actually, she broke two teeth, right at the gum line. I now have two teeth that were part of my wife's beautiful smile in a small paper cup stapled together on our pie safe. And the dentists, bless their hearts, are dancing around the blindingly obvious: that repairing the damage will be hard because at some point it will require the cooperation of a patient who is unable to cooperate.

How did it happen? She was pushed. One of the patients. Why'd he do it, asked one of the kids. I don't know, I answered; he has dementia. Literally, there is no reason. It's like being hit by a meteor, struck by lightning. It's an event with odds, and ours came up. Why couldn't we win the lottery? That would have been more fun. Now I have a wife with a damaged smile as if having a damaged brain isn't enough. This might fall into the category of piling on, if someone was doing it on purpose. But, I suspect, this is simply life as we know it. Fun at times, and brutally unpleasant at others.

If there's a bright side, it's that she's totally unaware of what happened. Mainly she's focused on her swollen lip. She harbors no feeling about the person who pushed her or the missing teeth. She eats, sleeps and goes about her business. Me? I thought I was keeping her safe. Now this. I'm angry, upset. Will it do any good? No. Everyone feels bad and my raging around won't help. I did play my guitar real loud last night in my bedroom and sang "Believe Me if All Those Endearing Young Charms" at the top of my lungs like a crazed metal head. That helped, as did crying. This morning I see the sun is up and there's fog on the pasture and it's another day. Onward.

Something to Keep

Thursday, May 9, 2019

A lot has been written about music and dementia and its palliative effect. It works. It makes people happy. My wife likes 1960s music, particularly the latter half of the '60s. Whenever we're in the car, I turn our streaming service in that direction and off we go down memory lane. She'll point at the radio and make happy sounds when a particularly memorable song comes on, and sometimes, she'll cry.

We listened to the music yesterday morning as we drove from Fredericksburg to New Braunfels for her latest appointment. The sky was dark and threatening rain, but the music made the sky less gray and the trip was easy. The appointment went well, and we were back in the car before we knew it. The radio came on and off we went down the road holding hands and letting the music play as we traveled.

At one point, Elvis was singing "Can't Help Falling in Love." I sang along under my breath and then I realized she was singing along, so I turned it up, and we sang together. And right at the end of the song, when he repeats *I can't help falling in love with you*, I looked over at her and she leaned in real close, and as the winds of music blew over the dying embers of her memories, the fire flared up. She looked me in the eyes and sang the words: *I can't help falling in love with you*. And I knew it was real and from the heart, a message from the deep. Sunshine on a gray day.

Around the Bend

Friday, May 10, 2019

I found myself with the need to kill some time yesterday. Which is an odd thing to say, especially as time becomes an increasingly precious commodity as you get older. But it was the case. I thought a retail establishment in Austin opened at 11 a.m. but when I arrived a note on the door said "back at one." I began pitching a mini-temper tantrum because it was an hour's drive in and an hour's drive back and I would have nothing to show for it. Then the light bulb went on and I realized it was almost lunch and a slow, leisurely meal would be a good thing and then I could go conduct my business. It seemed an adult approach, so I took it.

The lunch was nice, a muffuletta at the Specs just off Brodie. When I finished, I walked around the store. Shopping. It's something I learned from my wife. You look, and look, and make mental notes of cool things and catalog them for possible later purchase: personal, birthday, or Christmas. I think it's why she had so many friends. She was always thinking about them. I joined the party after the kids went off on their own. I became a good shopper, and as dates go, it was only moderately more expensive than a meal at a good restaurant and you had something to show for it.

We did a small reprise the other day. Our pharmacy is in the back of the local food store and she went in with me while I filled her prescription. Next, we stopped at the local dollar store, one of her favorite haunts. Going there had become almost a daily ritual at one point; I think it was her way of staving off the mental decline she felt coming. A routine to rely on. We went in, walked around, but I could sense a little confusion. Her grip on my hand was tight and there was no complaint as we left. It wasn't a day like it used to be, but it was a day and we were together and that was still something.

Addition and Subtraction

Wednesday, May 29, 2019

The annual Memorial Day camping trip went off without a hitch and without my wife in attendance. It was a first for me; she was forced to go by herself one year with the kids when I had to work unexpectedly. On this trip, I was there with my daughter and son-in-law to represent the family. But, while one generation lost a member, another generation was added. My goddaughter brought her 10-month-old son. One in, one out. The balance of the universe, I guess.

The weather was warm during the day and cool at night. And, in a blessed break, no rain fell. The Nueces ran clear and cold and its flood-formed bed offered us plenty of places to plop down and enjoy the water. Usually, I would have spent my time wandering around exploring, but on this trip all I really wanted to do was sit, and sit I did, right in the middle of a small piece of the river, in the shade of the sycamores.

The days had a nice rhythm to them. I slept reasonably well, and the company was lovely as usual. I brought a book to read and it stood me in good stead when I volunteered to babysit my son-in-law's sore-footed dog while he and my daughter went off to fish and explore. The dog slept, I read, and the afternoon passed on by. My wife was a good camper, well organized, and enduring. All I had to do this time was pull down the boxes and chairs and pack the car. I forgot a couple of things she would have remembered, but I'll get it next time, if there is a next time, which I'm sure there will be because, why not? Life goes on.

On to the OED

Thursday, May 30, 2019

Addled (a definition):

1. On my recent camping weekend, I wore comfortable driving shorts to the destination and changed into my work clothes upon arrival. We had mowing and camp preparation to do, and the tall grass was full of chiggers and ticks. Jeans were better than shorts. As I prepared to leave three days later, the comfortable driving shorts were nowhere to be found. I searched and searched, to no avail. Ultimately, I convinced myself that I'd worn something different. The next day, after my arrival home, I was running an errand, and there in the rearview mirror I saw my driving shorts huddled in the corner of the rear deck behind the backseat.

John is so addled he couldn't find his ass with both hands.

2. On the same drive home, at the end of the camping weekend, I stopped at a fast food diner. I laid my keys on the tray, arranged my food, and ate a leisurely meal as I read the book I'd brought along on the trip. At the end of the meal, I emptied the tray and stepped outside to continue the trip. A quick pat of the pockets told me all I needed to know about the location of my keys. They were in the trash. A plastic-gloved employee helped me dig through the garbage and there they were in someone's old drink cup. I dried them off and went on my way.

John is so addled he'd lose his head if it wasn't screwed on.

Two points isn't usually enough data to define a trend, but it does seem ominous. A possible defense would be to claim I was a genius, too involved in important thoughts to be bothered with minutia, but I'm not sure there's general support for that idea. It's more likely that I'm just a tired old man who had a relaxing weekend with friends and family and forgot to turn his brain back on when he was finished.

One Foot after Another

Friday, May 31, 2019

I took my wife for a walk. In a store. She used to do it on her own. Now she needs help. We walked all the aisles of the big box building, just looking. It took a good while. Then we went for a drive to another smaller store she used to frequent. We got out of the car, walked the aisles and just looked. Then we went home, our home, the house where we've lived since 2009. As we walked in the side door, she reflexively shut the lid on the washing machine. She continued into the front room, sat in her chair, ate a banana, and listened to music. After a while, she was ready to go.

We got in the car and drove back to her new home. I rang the bell for them to let us in and when they didn't come fast enough, she rang it again. Eventually, they came and let us in. She needed to use the restroom and I helped her get that done; then, we sat on a couch and held hands and watched a little mindless TV. At one point, she got up and walked to the double doors that led to the courtyard. She opened them and went outside.

I stood at the doors watching her as she walked, looking at the scenery in much the same fashion as she used to do at home when she walked around the gardens beneath the big oaks. When she got to the fountain in her new home beneath smaller oaks, she stopped and just looked. Then she did something surprising. She gestured with her left hand as though talking to someone and pointing out an interesting curiosity. There was a beauty to the gesture, the slight movement of her hand, the tilt of her head. In my mind, I could hear her voice, and for the tiniest of moments she felt whole again. It was a nice gift in an otherwise dreary journey.

Working on It

Friday, June 7, 2019

My endorphin generator is shot. I had a chat with the mechanic yesterday, but there's no timetable on when it will be fixed. I'm hoping it's only a software glitch, and that a bit of new code will get it back in working order. We ran through some options, and I'll give them a try. Meanwhile, there's no joy in Mudville, nothing to make my heart go pitter-patter, or any reason to be glad about anything. I'll take your word for it that sugar is sweet.

It's an odd way to live life, but it's doable. Luckily, the entire system didn't fail, and I can still remember a lot of joyful things. Children, grandchildren, walks on the beach, slow dances, kisses, and cool breezes on my skin. They have to be retrieved manually, however, and that's a bit of a pain. It's much better when the system is on full auto. Meanwhile, *keep on, keeping on* is the word of the day, or phrase, to be more precise.

I guess I should be grateful that the portion of my brain responsible for reporting system errors reported in and it got acknowledged. Otherwise, who knows what would have happened. The fix will take some time, and we'll know it's fixed, when it's fixed. Just visiting the mechanic seems to have a small salutary effect. It reminds me of our old well back in Alvin. Whenever I worked on it, I had to prime it to get it going. It never primed easily. It was a deep well and needed a lot of water. Since we needed water to live, I just kept at it until the solid suction kicked in. I guess it's the same way with this. I'll clean the points, get new code, keep priming, and one day the joy will flow unabated. Here's to tomorrow.

On the Way

Saturday, June 8, 2019

On my digital photo frame there occasionally appears a shot I took soon after we moved into our Hill Country home. It's a long look down a clean back porch. The cedar poles are fresh and new. The dirt that will become a garden is smooth and straight, machine scraped and groomed. It's a picture of potential, a house ready to become a home.

It's a different picture now. There's dust and dirt on the porch. The poles are still smooth, but they've grayed in the sun and show their age. The dirt has done what dirt does, grow things. There's a garden where trees and plants now abound, some planted but most are volunteers. A tall visiting sumac overshadows a dwarf crape myrtle. Windblown grass is shading a small rosemary plant. It's difficult to keep up with the volunteers, especially the grasses, most of which I've not yet learned to identify.

I've come to accept that the best I'll be able to do is maintain a balance between the volunteers and the planned plants. Give a little, get a little. Life is simply going to have its way and the most I'll be able to do is direct the course a bit and give myself some space to walk among the plants. It's actually a fair plan. Any gardener wants their garden growing and something that thrives must really want to be there. All I need to do is learn the names and pretend it's just what I wanted. After all, there are some battles that are simply not worth fighting, and compromise is the name of the game, and isn't that how a house becomes a home?

It's All in How You Look at It

Tuesday, June 18, 2019

The TV weather forecaster greeted me with the words *building heatwave* this morning. Apparently, it starts today. Oh, joy. At least I had yesterday to do some cool weather weed digging. Maybe I can do a bit more this morning. It seems weird to be so fixated on that subject, but that's where my life has ended up. I had no idea when I started out that the journey would take me to Garden Land. I guess I should have known. My great-grandmother on my dad's side was a constant gardener. Maybe it's a way of familiarizing yourself with the dust to which we all return.

Meanwhile, I took my bride to the dentist yesterday to see what could be done about her missing teeth. The options are slim to nothing because almost all of them require a sentient being who understands what's happening. At this point, that's not the case. Our dentist and our oral surgeon are confabbing and discussing options. The biggest issue is post-op. None of us know how she will react, although maybe that's a non-issue because her reaction to losing the teeth was almost non-existent.

This is another thing I never expected. I'm beginning to think that's the essence of life. A whole series of unexpected events. I should have taken improv classes as a kid. Although, maybe I did. After all, we moved every two years and I always had to adjust to that, and it seemed to work out. Still, it would be nice if the surprises were less catastrophic; although I guess when you sort them out they're probably fairly evenly matched. That's why they tell you it's a matter of perspective. Although, if you're about to be eaten by a grizzly, it's hard to remember to tell yourself: *Yeah, but I had so many good times.*

Counting

Tuesday, July 2, 2019

I t's been a soft summer so far. No blistering string of 100-degree days. No dried-out vegetation, brown hills, or barren streams. Instead the mornings are relatively cool, the fields green, the streams full, and every so often there is the promise and sometimes the actual delivery of rain. My freshly planted black-eyed Susans and purple cone flowers have prospered, and the fruit trees are full. Even my lone apple tree has fruit—big apples, not the tiny ones of years past.

On the personal front: I've gotten to visit my grandson; my daughter is doing well in her new position; my son-in-law got a promotion; my granddaughter is winning track medals; and I've gone to hear good music with my friends. We've had dinners together and I've been invited to travel with a fine group of folks this fall. Yesterday, I took a cooling dip in our pool and floated to music, watching the fair clouds drift by. These are good days by any measure.

The only fly in the ointment is my changed circumstances, a wife with dementia in a home not our own, although it's way more than a fly. It's more like an elephant or some beast of mythical proportions. That's why it's nice the world has conspired to show me a string of unending beauty and provide me with caring friends and family, and not just provide them, but stack them up in an amazing pile, acknowledging that tipping these scales requires serious weight. There's only one hitch. If someone could do something about the chiggers that would be nice, because they might be the straw that breaks the camel's back.

Feelin' Good

Saturday, July 6, 2019

There's this spirit-lifting thing that happens when you realize people are thinking about you. In a nice way, of course. I am speaking of those moments when you get a call or a text that basically says, "we request the pleasure of your company," and they mean it.

It happened earlier this month and four times this week. I was invited on a road trip with my son, got an invitation to watch a movie, got a text about meeting for a birthday lunch, received an invitation to share accommodations at a music festival, was notified that my daughter is coming for my birthday, and had a call from a cousin about a night out with dinner and music. I'm in with all of them. You have to feel blessed to be on the receiving end of such sweetness and thoughtfulness, and I do feel blessed.

It's easy, when you're down in the dumps, to sit at home like a lump and feel sorry for yourself. I've had a fair amount of practice. So, I know. My usual solution is simple and blindingly obvious. *Move*. Get up. Do things. And I do. It works. But sometimes it's a slow process and outside intervention is needed. So, I talk to people. That helps, too. But the payoff is the friends and family who come calling, unbidden, to visit or take you places or have you join them. Those are the finest gifts, no wrapping required, just the initiative to reach out. To which I say, thank you. With love.

Arrival Day

Thursday, July 11, 2019

And so starts another trip around the sun. A rainstorm in the night leading into a day full of small adventures, and a text from my son this morning, sent last night: "Thank you for introducing me to Little Feat. That is all." The storm broke a small branch from the flame leaf sumac and filled the back flowerbed with fallen petals from the crape myrtle, blown down and through the dog run. I was oblivious in my sleep.

I have to say I'm happy to be here, although if I weren't here, I don't think I'd have an opinion one way or the other. I wish my mother was here to bake me a yellow cake with chocolate icing, but that boat sailed in 1968. Later today, I'll have lunch with friends, and my daughter will drive in from Pearland to spend a day or two. It's nice to have people going out of their way to help celebrate my survival on the home planet. I hope that over the course of the coming year I can reciprocate enough to pay them back, but I don't think people give gifts in the hopes of pay back. Still, I can't just be a taker.

At this point there are a lot of years stacked up behind me and remembrance is a feature of the birthday celebration. As lives go, I'm guessing mine's about average. Born, worked, married, raised a family. Had better luck than some, worse luck than others. And I've done a fair number of interesting things. Plenty of blessings to count, lots in fact. I have a roof over my head, a little plot of land, a great family, and most of my faculties. And, this is really important: I have a passel of friends that I just love to pieces.

Time Travel

Monday, July 15, 2019

I had a lovely birthday weekend. My daughter made the long trip in from Pearland and we had lunch with friends on Thursday afternoon. They gave me a nice straw hat and a bottle of bourbon. I can now sit in the sun and drink without fear of a burn, unless I fall over and the hat comes off. My digital media account blew up with birthday wishes, and I think that's one of the nicest features it offers. I also got calls and texts from brothers and sons, and the day filled up nicely.

On Friday, my daughter and I went to see the movie "Yesterday." It was a weepy, happy, Beatles-filled musical. I rank it right up there with "Across the Universe," which is another slightly less weepy, but just as happy Beatles-filled musical. On Saturday we went for a walk and I logged it on my newest digital device, which now allows me to gaze at my wrist whenever I get a call or text just to see who is calling. Also, I can check the weather. Me and Dick Tracy. I may be old but I'm going to embrace the 21st century.

My daughter returned home Saturday, I got a massage, and then went to see my wife. Ordinarily you'd think seeing your spouse would be a happy occasion, but these almost never are. Melancholy is more apt. We sat in the shade beneath the big oaks and had a nice swing. On Sunday, more friends were in town to visit other friends, coincidental to my birthday, but still we all went out and had a nice Sunday brunch and they treated me. It was sweet. All that's left now is to set my sights on tomorrow as another year around the sun gets underway.

The Stuff of Life

Friday, July 19, 2019

I was eating dinner last night with family and friends and happened to notice a group of young women with their children at the table right across from us. One of them, a young girl about three or four, was wearing a Huipil dress, its bright embroidery set off against the dark green of the material. As I watched her move beside her mother, I was reminded of my wife who wore similar garments, mostly for casual wear, camping, hanging around the house, weekends at the beach.

In all our years of marriage, I never had a name for them. They were simply a ubiquitous style of dress that she wore, but a young Mexican couple who were part of our group last night knew the name "Huipil" and told me. I also never knew where she bought them. They were just there. A piece of clothing that defined her more than I ever imagined until she was no longer wearing it, and I saw one on a child in that random moment.

This morning I dug them out, sorting through the myriad of hanging clothes in her closet, just to look at them, hoping they hadn't somehow gone missing or were simply a figment of my own failing memory. But there they were. There are five. One white. One red. Two dark blue, and one purple. Some are thin from wear, others less so. It was surprising to see nearly 50 years of life encapsulated in those five dresses, but there they were, lying on the bed like empty cicada shells, their owner in some mysterious new world inside her own mind. Her memory filled the room, and I could almost hear her laugh.

The Musical Life

Tuesday, July 30, 2019

A friend of mine wrote a song once. He wanted to know what would happen to the songs he sung after he was gone[3]. I think I know, and it will happen before he leaves. This starts out a little bit technical but bear with me. A song, once heard, goes straight to the listener's auditory cortex, sweetened with pleasure for storage. There it is protected in a hardened area of the brain that is roughly equivalent to Superman's Fortress of Solitude, or Cheyenne Mountain, or the Black Panther's Wakanda. Disease and old age can beat against the doors, but the songs will always be there and then, when the rest of the brain resembles the ruins of World War II Dresden, someone will play that song and that little room will light up, untouched, with the music and memories fresh and alive.

Yesterday, I took my phone and small boom box speaker to visit my wife after her dinner. We sat outside on the porch and I turned on the old music. She slid close, held my hand and the music reached down into the deep secret place and unlocked those musical memories. It was warm and we were happy. She kissed my cheek. More than once. Another resident came out and asked if she could listen, too, and then sat on the opposite side of me when I agreed. She held my speaker as if it were a magic box and then handed it back for me to hold. Softly, she sang "Turn, Turn, Turn" with the Byrds, or maybe she was repeating Bible verses, and asked three times where I lived and how long I'd been married. Like a passenger on a long flight, I soon realized her head was resting on my shoulder as she listened.

We all sat there together, sophomores in high school, newlyweds, new parents, with friends and lovers, dancing dances danced long ago. There was peace and music in the air and in our minds, all because someone once wrote a song and sang it and we heard it and liked it. It's a good outcome when you think about it; a personal gift to help weather the storm and hold back the dying of the light. No rage. Just lyrics and melody, reminding us that there were lots of good things in life and these were some of them.

---

[3] Walt Wilkins, The Songs I've Sung, Vigil

Smile

Thursday, August 1, 2019

It's interesting to walk into my pantry and find a shelf lined with jam and peaches I canned with help from my son. We had two sessions at his house in Houston and one at mine, where I went it alone. I have 16 pints now, and he has six because we split the take at his house. One of the batches was spiced with cinnamon and my granddaughter said it smelled like cobbler. We also canned a Zesty Peach BBQ Sauce. Not all the jars set, but we have four pints of that. It complemented the salmon we ate for dinner. I labeled most of the jars last night to make them look official.

I got my first taste of canning last year when I took my peaches to a friend's house where we peeled, pitted and cooked. I still have a few jars from that 2018 effort sitting on the shelf. This year they came over to my house and picked their own batch and canned them up with their recipe. I have no idea how many jars they filled, but they seemed happy and the picture they sent looked good. It's a nice result for the old peach tree, and next year I'll start the canning as soon as the first peaches ripen. Although it's fun to give people small bags of fresh peaches because eating a fresh peach is a real treat.

Next up I'm going to try some strawberries and maybe make some applesauce. I'll have to buy the fruit at the store. I'm also thinking of my own garden once again. My son canned some pickles and peppers from his garden, and I can do the same. We'd stopped our official food gardening when my wife's illness progressed, but I can start back up. The beds lie fallow just waiting for a loving hand. I can eat some and can the rest. I think she'd like that. I'll tell her when I see her this evening.

In the Garden of My Friends

Friday, August 2, 2019

I went to see a friend's garden yesterday. It's a lovely patchwork of trails and trees and raised beds with new plantings, old plantings, and family plantings. It's the sort of garden where you can walk the same path three times and be surprised three times in the same season. It's a garden with stories and he told me the stories as we walked, about the gifts and the disappointments. It's a garden where you can just pause and stand and look, and we did.

It made me think of all the gardens of my friends. How each one of them reflects the people tending the plants, planting them, watching over them. And how each of the gardens or landscapes or whatever they're called, comes with a house, and the houses are lovely and well decorated but almost without fail, everyone always wants to go outside when they visit. They want to stand in the shade of trees, to hear water running, and see blooms bend in the wind. Even in the fury of a storm, most people still look outside.

A nice outside area was one of the reasons I picked this memory care home for my wife. I went to visit her yesterday after dinner and found her sitting outside with two of her friends. They were on the porch listening to the wind in the old oaks. They made room for me and I sat with them. I told her about our friend's garden and in better days she would have been there, and loved it, too. But better days in that regard are past. Now we only have each other, in a wordless communion, with a seat on the porch in the shade.

The Team

Saturday, August 10, 2019

I have an office upstairs with built-in bookshelves and a place for my records. I've had one in every home we owned. We always referred to it as the Library because we collected books. In almost every instance, it was where I went to write and read and just get away, because marriage needs space and pauses where both parties have room to pursue their pursuits. Mine was books and writing and the occasional guitar playing.

The office is upstairs because my wife, when she was playing with the floor plan for our new home, realized there was no space for one downstairs, given that a large portion of our foundation was allocated to the breezeway that's a signature feature of the house. We toyed with giving it up and going to a traditional layout, but we liked it, although, truth be told, it was probably more me than her. So, the office went upstairs, and I was happy it did because I got exercise climbing the stairs and the view from the window was exceptional.

The office sits largely unused these days. It acts as a bedroom when my daughter or son comes to visit, but I moved my computer gear downstairs a while back along with my guitars. The records and books are still up there, and I keep thinking I'll make it into a listening room, but the question is why. I no longer need space; if anything, I've got too much. I'd like to talk with my wife about it, because she always was good with repurposing things in the house, but our conversations these days largely consist of holding hands. Maybe the next time we're together I can think about it and she'll move next to me and a solution will present itself.

Hit or Miss

Thursday, August 15, 2019

The rain came yesterday. Missed me. I could see the storms coming. And going. Nary a drop fell on the old homestead. More scattered showers are expected today. But the term *scattered* means just what it says. I'll feel blessed if the raindrops fall on me during this cycle. Although, truthfully, I feel blessed most days. My kids still talk to me, I have fine friends, and most of my faculties. So, while getting rain would be nice, it's not a make-or-break proposition at this point.

Things could change, however, because that's what life offers—change. You try to be ready, on your toes, flexible, ready to go either way, but sometimes change is so radical and overwhelming that no amount of preparation helps. It's off to the dumps and you're down in them, and a missed rainstorm feels like nature is piling on and you sympathize with Job. All this I know from practical experience, having been there. Luckily, I found my way out. With help. Important to note, because climbing out of the dumps on your own is tricky business. A helping hand is almost always a good deal.

That being said, there are no dumps in sight at the moment. Courses are charted and the way forward is clear. It might rain today, or it might not. Either way, I'm good. I can still stand on the porch and smell the sweetness of a wet earth in the early morning when the air is cool and fresh and know that somewhere, for someone, it rained and it was good.

A Blast from the Past

Saturday, August 17, 2019

When I came home last night from dinner with friends, I found boxes of pictures on our dining room table, a two-thirds completed scrapbook, and about six empty scrapbooks waiting their turn to be filled with pictures. They came from the bedrooms now occupied by my son, who is doing a deep cleaning of his rooms across the dog run. The closet he now uses was where his mother stored our pictures and her scrapbooks. These are the last of her collections to come out.

To say my wife enjoyed scrapbooking would be to understate her pleasure and the intensity with which she practiced the hobby. Her scrapbooks are works of art, a nonpareil look back at our life and times, a 20th century version of an illuminated manuscript. She went off with friends on scrapbooking weekends, she scrapbooked at home, and back when it was still the rage, she visited Hruska's general store on Highway 71 to check out their scrapbook section. That section is long gone, and scrapbooking, while still practiced, is no longer a major obsession with the hobby-minded. And then somewhere along the line, her disease robbed her of the desire and ability to practice her craft.

But I still have her scrapbooks with their annotations and delicately worked pages, and boxes of pictures organized and ready for their turn to be sorted, selected and pasted. The completed scrapbooks are on a small bookshelf in the front room ready for perusal, and the boxes of pictures are waiting for me to do something. At the moment, I'm sort of at a loss, because I feel like anything I do will be roughly equivalent to someone trying to replicate the Book of Kells. I guess you always have to start somewhere. Those empty scrapbooks may be her way of saying, get busy, boy.

Put Your Little Hand in Mine

Thursday, August 29, 2019

Since my wife went into memory care, one of the struggles has been the visits themselves. Frontotemporal dementia with an emphasis on speech means no language, which means no casual chit-chat, which means no one hears what I've been up to, or asks how-was-your-day. Gradually, as I've read up on this, and talked to friends who have visited, I've discovered strategies to make the visit more rewarding and less depressing, if that's really possible. First, there's music, and secondly, pictures. Her scrapbooks are a treasure trove of memories. Finally, there's the tactile bit.

I do her nails. She likes it. Mostly, I clean and trim. I knew she'd caught on the day I finished one hand and she calmly plopped the other hand on the arm of the chair. I'm going to begin buffing and polishing on the advice of a friend. I also started massaging her hands and forearms. Last week I slathered on a bit of hand cream, vanilla and patchouli. The latter is an old scent from the days of her youth. I thought it might spur memories, but with no language between us I had no way to suggest that she take a sniff.

Then several days ago, as the music played and we sat together like old times, I watched her put her hand to her face with the middle finger gently touching the tip of her nose, and she breathed in, with purpose. The she took her other hand and did the same thing. After doing that several times, she looked over at me, moved one hand to her face, and then quickly rubbed both hands together in front of her toward me. I knew in that instant she had discovered the scent and knew from whence it came. I felt as though the fog had lifted and for a brief moment, once again, the two of us stood together in a well-lit clearing, connected.

Doing for the Least of These

Friday, August 30, 2019

I took care of a small job for my cousin this past week: bringing water to heifers. It was relatively easy. I walked out of my gate, turned right and went into my cousin's pasture. Pulled the hose out of the big tank, placed it in the watering trough and let it run for an hour. I doubt the heifers even knew I did it. They just walked up, drank, and went back to eating. The deer probably stole a drink late at night and maybe even a raccoon or fox. I wasn't watching.

It was fun doing the job. Sometimes, after I put the hose in the trough, I just stood and watched the water in the tank and the goldfish tasked with keeping it clean. It was also fun watching the water fall out of the pipe after the windmill had drawn it up out of the ground. Peaceful. My other job was to shut the windmill off if the wind ever got too high, but it never did. I shut it off once when a thunderstorm threatened. It never materialized. I turned it back on. The wind blew. The blades spun. Up came the water. Science.

My cousin is home now. The heifer watering job is over. I'm left with doing the normal stuff. Feeding the cats, watering plants, and visiting my wife. Now that I think about it, maybe that's part of the reason I feel so dumpy sometimes. I still feel guilty that I farmed her out to a place where I pay folks to take care of her. Of course, I've been told I'm also supposed to take care of myself and while I did reasonably well as a 24/7 caretaker, it wasn't sustainable. That's a conundrum and, while the human mind is a wonderful thing, a conundrum can give it fits and before you know it all of the machinery is out of whack and you feel like an Edvard Munch painting. But we soldier on. Watering, feeding, and trying to be grateful that a loved one is well cared for, even if by strangers.

Off in the Distance

Saturday, August 31, 2019

I had a dream last night. It was long and vivid. I remember snippets this morning. None worth repeating. As I think about them, they get soft around the edges and smaller. In a few days, they'll be long gone. I could write them down. I did that once when I had a few disturbing dreams. But I lost the papers and those dreams are gone as well. It's probably for the best. Be they good or bad, I doubt we're meant to hold on to our nighttime dreams. The bottom line is that I woke up fairly well rested. I think that's a good sign. I clocked in at about seven hours.

It rained a bit yesterday as I drove to Fredericksburg to visit my wife. Just a spattering. Off in the distance I could see someone getting a good dose. The responsible cloud was gray from sky to ground. A summer storm of the usual type. I remember seeing lots of them when I was first married and still trekking around to play slow-pitch softball. I'd watch the cloud as I drove always hoping it was falling on someone else's field and I would get to play. It usually worked out that way and the game would go on. But sometimes, not. You'd arrive. The field would be a sea of mud. And off you'd go back home.

Sometimes life feels like a dream. An uncollected smattering of memories boinging around in my head. None really worth remembering, but there they are, and I get to sort through them. Maybe that's one way to get through hard times: pretend it's a dream. Maybe that's how my wife views the world. A dream. Just memories without words, if you can imagine that, growing soft around the edges. Maybe that's why she's so glad to see me and other people she knows when we come to visit. We're something real and she doesn't need words.

The Other Side

Tuesday, September 3, 2019

I 'm unclear as to how a 66-degree morning temperature can immediately lift my spirits. But it does and it did. Today is trash day and as I went outside to do the chore, there it was: coolness. I guess moroseness doesn't stand a chance against crisp morning air. I was all set to write about feeling dumpy and thinking no one really wants to hear about it when the simple act of going outside changed my tune. The fact of the dumpiness still remains, but now it seems a vestige of something unpleasant rather than a state of mind.

The whole thing hinged on a week's worth of me being unable to get moving. It took a Saturn 5 worth of energy to get me out of my chair this past Saturday and on the road. Once there, I was glad I did. Just being in the car was a tonic of sorts. I ran errands and bought a set of guitar strings. The parabola of the journey ended at a winery listening to music, with the unexpected benefit that I saw a lot of people I hadn't seen in a while and they were people I liked. It gave me a good bounce for my Sunday trip to Houston, where we celebrated two birthdays and watched a football game with dear friends of long standing.

There's a lesson here, I suppose. Probably encapsulated in the tried-and-true wisdom of "this, too, shall pass." Yeah, but it's easy to say that on the backside of the storm, and a little bit harder to believe when the winds are howling and it's all dark and nasty. In retrospect, it wasn't nearly as bad as that, just gray and cloudy and nothing I haven't seen before. I pretty much knew my way out. It was just the execution that needed doing, and I did it. Now, my reward is a nice morning and a hot cup of tea. All that needs doing at the moment is to feed the cats to stave off a revolt in the animal kingdom.

Three Things

Wednesday, September 4, 2019

Yesterday's cool air pulled me out into the yard. I did some work. A minor amount. Weeding mostly in the beds around the big oaks. I've kept them pretty much under control this spring and summer. Winter work will be minor, and we'll be ready for the flower show, come next spring. There was also a solarization project to check. It went well. The plastic superheated the ground, killed off the weeds and left me with a clear patch of dirt. I might make it into a path or plant a little grass. Still undecided. Grass probably.

The power-washed porches still look sparkly. My handy, battery-powered blower works wonders to keep them relatively free of dirt and debris. Previously, my wife did the chore with a broom. That blower was probably the only cleaning appliance I bought for her that was truly appreciated. As her dementia worsened and she stopped doing the chore, I took over. The sound of the little blower would bring her outside, and she'd applaud with delight. It's nice to make your wife happy. She'd do the same when I mowed. She enjoyed a tidy yard, and I was a willing servant.

The cameras I'd installed to watch my wandering wife are still capturing images of wildlife. A little fox has been spotting on the drive. He usually comes early in the morning around five, but yesterday he was there about 1:30 a.m. I'll probably move the camera this weekend to get a better view and see where he's going. It's interesting to see what happens in your yard while you're asleep. A fox is a nice treat. As visitors go, he passes through, leaves the occasional scat, and keeps to himself. Not bad for a neighbor.

A Weekend Well Spent

Monday, September 9, 2019

Got in the way-back machine and drove to Houston this weekend. The occasion was the ceremony promoting my son-in-law to Lt. Colonel in the Army. His wife and mom pinned on the oak leaf, and then we went to the house for a little celebration with family and friends. There was a nice cake and decorations, and it was a fun time all the way around. Later this year he'll get a doctorate in Education. I think it's safe to say he's an accomplished young man.

Next up: a trip to the old campus to watch my collegiate team play their home opener. It was a success. We did notice that the old group had shrunk to four. Two of the wives were missing (not permanently, just not there), several friends had moved away or were too ill to travel, and one of our group had passed. I guess we will keep on keeping on, but a lot of the attraction was meeting up before the game to have a drink, share some food and enjoy one another's company. I'm guessing we can still do that without having to sit in a stadium parking lot, although the games are fun, too.

Later that evening we repaired to one of the friend's home for the night's lodging, had more good conversation, a taste of cognac, and then off to bed. In the morning we ate a fine breakfast, then said our goodbyes. When next we gather, it will be beside a river to celebrate the wedding of a child. More of the extended group will be there and it should be a nice weekend. I'm looking forward to it. We will eat, drink, and be merry, which, if you know any of us, is something we enjoy doing and are well practiced at. The only difference being, the intensity has dropped off a bit. You could say that reflects our maturity, but aging bodies are the more likely culprits.

Here and There

Monday, September 23, 2019

I spent Saturday evening beside a river beneath the spreading limbs of a big oak celebrating the nuptials of a young couple. The bride was the daughter of close friends of long-standing. There was music and dancing and spirits of both types, liquid and angels of love. Everyone was happy, and if otherwise, they kept it to themselves.

I spent Sunday evening on a swing beneath a small grove of oaks at the memory care facility with my wife. We had music playing, but no dancing. We sat alone, held hands, and shared an occasional kiss. The crowds are long gone. Most of the folks who swept us off into our own marital adventure are departed, with the exception of those close friends who sat beside me on Saturday.

It was a weekend of contrasts. Young and old. Fresh and tired. Arcs of all kinds. At the Saturday event there were children everywhere. They added considerably to the festive air. Those of us who are older remembered when the children's parents were infants, and we smiled. On Sunday, the young were the caregivers, and one of them held my wife's hand as I left for the evening, an angel of love dressed as a stranger. Today the sun is bright, we're back to our own devices, and the adventure continues.

A Word from the Front

Friday, September 27, 2019

I had a jam-packed afternoon yesterday. I bought three books, a battery for my riding mower, two air filters for my car (engine, cabin air), and two birthday cards. I installed the air filters and then got an oil change. I started the first book last night. I'll mail the cards this morning. In the course of doing all this, I picked up a prescription. I found it to be oddly exciting. "Odd," because these are relatively normal events that people do all the time; and "Exciting" because in previous days the thought of doing even one of them was roughly akin to thinking about climbing the Himalayas. Insurmountable.

The difference-maker: a morning visit to my counselor. It was a rough drive in, and at one point I nearly turned around and went home. But I persevered, made it to the appointment, and unburdened myself. I even slipped in a couple of weepy moments. I'm not sure why, but I always apologize when it happens, as if crying because my wife has dementia and it upsets me might be a rude thing to do. Anyway, he always sits quietly while it happens, then when it's all out, we start talking, and when it's over, I feel better. Thus, the up and at 'em exuberance of my afternoon.

I'm pretty sure it will carry over. Today I've got another busy morning planned. I'm taking my bride to the doctor for a little check-up to keep a runny nose from becoming more troublesome, and in the afternoon, I plan on hooking up that battery and firing up the old riding mower. The on-going trick will be to keep moving. If I don't, I'll start slipping in the mud and bury myself up to the axles, again. Of course, there's a certain inevitability to all this. Even with the best of intentions, the "again" will happen. But that's why the counselor is there: to keep the mud from swallowing me whole.

The Mower's Tale

Saturday, September 28, 2019

It's a picture. Eighteen people sitting on a stone wall. When I look at it, I can see my entire married life from the day I met my wife until now. Fifty years of friendships. I can see courtship, first homes, new homes, children, grandchildren, vacations, sporting events, schools, music, parties, dancing, weddings and funerals. Life. Hugs and kisses. Happy days, sad days, hard days, and good days. I can see all the things that happened because one day a girl stopped to hear me sing.

Of course, this isn't the end; our story is still being told. The picture, for instance, is missing one couple and two spouses. Illness kept them home. To keep them with us, we thought about them and talked about them and kept them in our hearts. I don't even suppose it's too late to add new folks to the picture. After all, the picture represents a lot of lives, and eventually someone in those lives will meet all of us and find a spot in our hearts and a place in the next picture. That's how the picture has grown over the years and will continue to grow and evolve.

In the past, I've worried about the secret to friendship, afraid I was somehow missing the skills needed to have them. Then I looked up one day and I realized they were all around me and I was finding more of them all the time. That was pretty exciting. Of course, I still worry that my social skills need work, and that I talk too much, but as long as you have people willing to work with you, that's pretty cool. Because in the end, I have no control over what someone thinks; all I can do is smile and do the best I can.

Being There

Saturday, October 5, 2019

I was twelve years older than my youngest brother. Occasionally, I'd get to pat him to sleep while singing a little lullaby that my momma sang.

> *Go to sleepy little baby.*
> *Go to sleepy little baby.*
> *When you wake you'll patty, patty cake.*
> *And ride a shiny little pony.*

And that was it. I just repeated it over and over in the dark, while rhythmically patting my brother's back. It was a nice melody. I also did it for my children when they were infants. It was a peaceful moment in the dark, with your baby, helping sleep to come.

I was reminded of it yesterday as I sat with my wife in her room at the memory care facility. We'd done our routine of handwashing, fingernail trimming, and hand massage. We'd walked outside. We'd sat on the porch. She'd looked at a photo album. Now we were just sitting quietly, listening to the music. As we did, she started nodding off, until finally she got up and moved to her bed. She picked up my bag of supplies and the photo album and moved them to a nearby chair. Then she took off her shoes and crawled into bed. I moved to the chair beside her bed. As she drifted off to sleep, looking over at me, I turned off the light and took my leave.

It's a strangely rewarding business ushering people into and out of life, holding their hands, patting them on the back, singing little lullabies. As a young parent, it gave me peace at the end of a long day. Now, as an old man, it does the same, except it's more than a day that's ending. But in either case, as we slip into the dark of night, it has to be comforting knowing there's someone sitting beside you, there in the dark.

The First Hint

Monday, October 7, 2019

Morpheus departed this morning around 2:30 a.m. I rose from my bed. Checked the outside temperature. It was 71 degrees. I stepped outside. It was muggy. I retreated. Went back to bed. Morpheus' younger cousin, the sandman, came. I woke at 5:30 a.m., dawdled until 6, and then got after it. Pitter-patter. This time the temperature said 67 degrees. I stepped outside. The first breath of fall touched my cheeks. Alleluia.

The morning promises to be busy. I'm taking my wife to see the neurologist. We'll have a long morning together. A friend has volunteered to ride with us. There are times on these trips when an extra pair of hands comes in handy, helping with someone whose mind is not quite what it used to be. We've known this couple since we bought our first home in 1975. They lived right down the street, next to my mother-in-law. Now, here we are in Johnson City, and they literally still live right down the street on the road to Blanco.

It's nice to have friends who step up, and all of ours have. It seems as though the air is a sea of helping hands, hugs, kisses, and lots of love. I do believe I could waltz across Texas on the goodwill spread around in our favor. At this point, there is no danger I will be allowed to wallow in the slough of despondency. There is always someone beckoning to me, offering their company, treating me to a meal, just being there, making sure that a hard road is a little less trying.

The Grind

Tuesday, October 8, 2019

Perky weather this morning. The temperature is 53 degrees at the old homestead. Where once there was sun, however, there is now darkness. Our daylight is shortening. Surely, the cool weather is here to stay. They say another front is due this weekend. It may be the double-hammer that clearly brings us fall. I'm ready. The heat was late in arriving this year, but when it did it was blistering. I'm glad it's gone for now.

The trip to the doctor went well yesterday. My neighbor's helping hands made it a lot less stressful than previous visits. Our doctor and a young intern interviewed us, asked questions, made notes and told me things to watch for in the coming days and months as the edifice of her brain continues slowly to crumble. We had a nice lunch at a local cafeteria and on the drive home my wife nodded off. We avoided the nausea of previous trips. That was good. I'm certain having her friend in the car with us helped.

Today will be filled with not much of anything. I have a few errands to run. I'll pick a bit on my guitar, and read a book. The one on Beethoven's symphonies came. It's a reprint of the third edition that was originally published in 1898. It will be good to lose myself in a slow movement of music and try to understand where it's going and why, because right now it feels as though there's a bit of sand in the gears of the universe and the music of the spheres is grinding along slightly out of tune.

Up and Down,

Thursday, October 10, 2019

I had a wonderful time with friends last night, listening to music, drinking a beer. A married couple of longstanding made a surprise appearance. We hugged and sat together. After the show was over, we tarried outside talking to one another and to the musicians we knew. The night air was soft and the conversations happy. Eventually, everyone slipped away to continue their lives. My long drive home was uneventful, and sleep came easily.

The morning after is slightly less bright. The air is muggy. Gray clouds are hinting at rain. I'm alone in my home. It's starting to look a little cluttered, which is a bad sign. I know the remedy. I just need to take the medicine. A good breakfast will help. I have some farm fresh eggs from the hens of friends. They need to be washed, but then they're ready for the skillet. That's appealing. I had a hard time with eggs as a child, but I got over it.

This is probably another one-foot-after-the-other portion of my current journey. Hardly exciting, but necessary. One day at a time, as they say. Nothing to be gained in wallowing or feeling sorry for myself. It's just that I'm so good at it. Maybe because it's easy. Anyone can do the easy stuff. The challenge is slipping past it and carrying on in good spirits, picking up a guitar, banging out a tune, and being grateful for friends who feel the same way.

That Time of Year

Friday, October 11, 2019

I woke to the rhythm of the rain this morning. Along with it, a north wind is blowing, and cooler air is flowing down finally to chase away summer. Although, I hear tell the heat may reappear next week. Still, I think we can say this is fall and it's welcome. I enjoy turning into the dark corner of the year, with the shortened days. I'm ready for winter, although there's little to do in preparation for it. At least not in this part of the country.

The cold front rain will help water-in the corn gluten I spread to act as a pre-emergent. I'd been trying to do it manually, but it seems as though you can never really get enough water down. And it's particularly difficult to reach every inch of exposed ground. Nope. You need the rain. And rain it did. I'm particularly excited to see what effect it will have on my driveway, which is composed of decomposed granite. Over the years it's proven fertile ground. Let's hope this changes the pattern. I really felt odd having to mow my drive.

Yesterday, I attacked my clutter, which makes it sound as though it's a little goblin living in the corner of my front room. Actually, it was just all the debris that marks my passing through the house. I have more to do. For instance, there's a cooler that needs returning to the attic. For weeks it has sat on a counter in the utility room. No harm, no foul, I guess. But my wife would have insisted on its departure. I'll do it in her honor. Besides, I take her point. A cleared-off countertop does make the house look nicer.

Re-arranging Deck Chairs

Wednesday, October 16, 2019

I went to visit my wife yesterday around 6 p.m. Our son was with me. When we arrived we discovered she was sound asleep. She'd finished dinner and gone to bed. We checked in on her and left without disturbing her. She was breathing deep and restful, and the sleep seemed more important. I arrived home in time to see the Astros defeat the Yankees, although to be honest, I only watched the top half of the ninth inning. I can't watch the playoffs this year. I've reached my disappointment quota for live action drama. I just want to hope they win and read about it if they don't.

Later that evening, I went outside to bring the cat food in for the night. Too late. A possum was already at the table. I walked up and he just sat there. He was small, but I wasn't looking for a fight. I just wanted the cat food. He could go get grubs. Eventually, he figured out I wasn't leaving, and when I sidled around to the side and gave him an escape route, he took it. I brought the cat food inside.

Earlier in the day, I completed the cleaning of the driveway edge opposite the front flower bed. Hoed and raked. It's hardly a page-turner in the book of my life, but what is, these days? There's still a lot to do, and I'm going to do it. I think I'll keep on cleaning down the drive toward the gate, and then work my way back up the other side and leave the center for last. When all is said and done, I'll have a spiffy clean driveway. And the kids will be like, well, if it makes him happy...

Sweet Dreams

Friday, October 18, 2019

The last of the rosemary has finally bit the dust. It's now a big brown potential fire-bomb sitting at the western corner of the back porch. Removing it will be an itchy, tiresome mess. Oh, well, that's the life of a plant tender. The same thing is happening beneath the crape myrtle in the front. Once, it was a smallish tree surrounded by Turks caps, rock roses and salvia. Gradually, they all disappeared, shaded out until now only a scraggly, sun-starved salvia remains.

This is when I could use some power tools. Cutting down the rosemary by hand will be laborious. But chainsaws, though labor-saving, can also be disastrous in the hands of amateurs, and I'm nothing in that area if not an amateur. Plus, there's the cost of owning and maintaining a device that you might use once or twice a year. Nope. I think it's going to be me, a hand saw and a pair of pruning shears, working slow and steady. Seems a safer bet.

Meanwhile, I'm still amazed at how the tenor of our yard has changed over the ten years we've been here. Plants have come and gone, moved around, succeeded, and failed. The trees have grown large, died off or died out. It would be fascinating to watch a time-lapse film of the changes. The closest I can come, however, is the one that runs in my head. Luckily, I can watch that one anytime I want. I particularly like the bits where my wife is out and about passing through the landscape, digging beds, and watering. I bet the plants miss her being around. I know I do.

And We Dance

Monday, October 21, 2019

After hearing some friends play music on Sunday afternoon, I finished the day with my wife. We held hands, sat outside, and took a short walk. The latter always takes place on the sidewalk that circles the courtyard at her memory care facility. It's a little over 200 feet long, almost in a square, and passes through a grove of smallish oaks on the far side, opposite the house. The yard in the center is Bermuda with five crape myrtles.

Yesterday, as we neared the far-left corner, she took me off the path and over toward the big fence. We stood there for a second, then turned and headed back. About halfway down the walk, as we moved back to the house, she stopped again. This time she put her toes right up against the edge of the sidewalk facing the fence. I did the same. Then, she did a moonwalk-like shuffle backwards until her heels touched the opposite edge of the walk. I did it with her. We then turned and continued the walk. We did this twice more on successive circles.

Obviously, there's no way to get an explanation. It's all up to the imagination. I like to think of it as a little dance. She loved line dancing to the Harlem Shuffle when we were regular invitees to a Krewe Ball in New Orleans and it felt a little bit like that, only without the music and with just a few short steps and slower. Maybe the song was playing in her mind. Maybe I wanted it to be playing in her mind. Maybe I wish I could ask her what we were doing. Maybe it doesn't matter. Maybe doing it is all that counts. Maybe it was just something to think about as I drove home in the dark.

First Glance

Wednesday, October 23, 2019

Sometimes, in the morning, when the light's just right and the air is still, I like to stand on the front porch and watch the yard. Everything is golden. The dew sparkles. The chill of the night is just leaving. It's the start of the day, that little pause at the top, before everything kicks into gear, and the air stirs, and the birds begin to move. In that moment of stillness, silence, and light, it's all potential.

I could take a picture and sometimes I do, but it's never the same as the picture that lives in my brain. Which is, I guess, what makes memories special, and why I never wanted a video camera when the kids were young. I didn't want to spend my time with them watching through a viewfinder. I can watch their movies anytime I want just by closing my eyes and harkening back. But that's another story.

I like to look, and watch, and appreciate. Mornings are good for that. Appreciating. And watching. And setting the tone. Aligning the spirit, bracing oneself for what may or may not be ahead. Being thankful for what you've got. Seeing beauty. A big mix of stuff that's all there in that one moment when you step outside into the cool morning air and take a slow, deep breath.

Domestic Chores

Thursday, October 24, 2019

I brought home my wife's clothes and washed them last night. The facility where she lives has industrial washers and driers, but her clothing never come out smelling as fresh as I like. Incontinence has a way of doing that. When I finished, I folded them up in a laundry basket and drove back to the home. It was late, but that's okay, there wasn't much traffic and it's a really easy, short drive.

Once there, I took the clothes into my wife's room and put them in the chifforobe that passes for a closet. Her room was dark, she was asleep and had been that way since I was in earlier to visit and get the clothes. As I waited to talk with one of the aides, however, my wife came out of her room, disturbed no doubt by my short visit. She saw me, said, "Oh, good," and came over to me. She kissed me on the cheek, and we sat on one of the couches.

As we did, I watched the aides gradually gather up all of the patients and get them to their respective rooms. Where once there were four or five people shuffling through, finally there were none. They went to their beds, one at a time, all done peacefully and quietly. Eventually the aide came for my wife. She had gone to sleep earlier in her clothes but now it was time for nightwear. We walked to her room, I kissed her goodnight, and the aide took her inside to change and with that, her focus shifted. I made my way out, drove home, and put myself to bed, making a mental note that I needed to learn how to use fabric softener, because dryer sheets just aren't good enough.

Tripping

Monday, November 4, 2019

It was a good weekend. I went to Houston to help my daughter with her children she's fostering to adopt while her husband was out of town on family business. We fell backwards in time, went to visit her brother and his family, and watched a lot of animated movies in between. The trip home was fairly zippy. Coming off Beltway 8, I decided to take the Hardy Toll Road out to Brookshire. It parallels Interstate 10 and allows me to miss most of the multi-lane madness close to town. Lots of construction, but no real problems.

The big highway was easy. People in Texas still have a problem understanding what "Left Lane for Passing Only" means. But once I realized they can't hear me griping at them, I stopped griping at them. Better for the blood pressure. The biggest hiccup came south of Austin where I ran into the crowd leaving the U.S. Grand Prix at Circuit of the Americas. Wow. It took a lot of time to make it past the one light where they all come out onto Highway 71. Not the best design. I hope there are other exits. After that, it was just driving into the sun.

At home the cats came out to say hello, the sun set, I ate dinner, watched TV and went to bed. Slept right through the night. That's a big deal these days. Apparently, sleep is useful. I'm trying to get as much as I can, within reason. If you get too much you're depressed. I'm still sad, for sure, but I don't think it's edged over into full-scale depression. Although, they're actually fuzzy on the guidelines. It's sort of like that song we used to sing in Cub Scouts about the Duke of York. "When you're up, you're up, and when you're down, you're down. And when you're only half-way up, you're neither up nor down." It makes me feel good just writing that.

Today's Concern, Nothing

Wednesday, November 6, 2019

In the pasture yesterday, we had a festival-sized gathering of birds. The starlings came en masse to pick the leavings off the dead plants, swarming across the ground to gather up the seeds as they prepared for winter, I suppose. My only preparation has been to can a few peaches, mainly for entertainment, however, as opposed to sustenance. Watching the birds, I felt derelict in my winter-preparation duties. Back in the day, when I used to go hunting, we would have had venison in the freezer by now and eventually a few waterfowl. But those were expensive sports and hardly qualified as living off the land.

This morning I woke to rain. It came last night, and the sky is still gray and cloudy this morning. Perhaps more will come today, although I've not heard any weather forecast. Living as I do outside the city, I have no need for local news. Any weather big enough to be a threat will cause my phone to light up. So, I no longer watch the news at 6 or 10 p.m. I'm certain the local stations hardly notice my absence, since I'm well out of the range of their target demographic.

Besides, at the given time I'm usually on my way to visit my wife. We meet post-dinner, stroll through the gardens, listen to music, and sit outside, weather permitting. Lately, with the time change and early onset darkness, I've been able to help her get ready for bed. It's a much more relaxed process these days than it was previously, when I was locking cabinets, flipping breakers to deaden appliances, and sleeping on the couch to watch the door. Her universe is a manageable size now and seems to fit her well. That's good. It appears we're both adjusting. And neither of us much cares what the weather does.

A Toast to Tomorrow

Saturday, November 9, 2019

Today marks the end of the beginning. Or maybe the beginning of the end. Whatever. It's the one-year anniversary of the day I consigned my wife to the care of strangers. The arc of her disease had brought her back to a childhood of sorts, the big difference being she still knew how to drive and walk off, and was unafraid to do either. In her damaged brain, caution literally had been thrown to the wind. She does without thinking. Acts without understanding. I had parented three times before, and stayed up nights to feed and comfort, but this was different and more dangerous. It was a hard decision, but I knew she would be better protected in a home with 24-hour care.

That I had the option at all was a result of good fortune and luck born in grief. Twelve years earlier, as my father lay dying, I realized his military career and follow-on second career had left him with all the tools he needed to care for himself in his later years. Not buckets of money, just good insurance. At the time, we had no such fallback. So, I bought some. Long-term care insurance with no lifetime cap. Being four years older than my wife, I thought it was for me. Maybe, in a sense, it was. Dear Prudence, thanks.

Anyway, here we are, a 21st century couple living apart. Her in a nice home with servants; me just down the road at the homestead. It's a wee bit different than we envisioned our retirement, and obviously I wish we'd had another outcome. But I learned a long while back, the only thing you can do with the future is live it when it gets here. And that's what we're doing, one day at a time, making our way across the stage to what we hope will be a graceful exit. And while we do it, I'm grateful for luck and the friends and family walking with us.

Dreaming

Monday, November 18, 2019

I plumbed this past week. I'd like to say it was the depths of my soul, but it was merely the bathroom sink. An incessant drip is no more. The nighttime is once again silent. I put it off for a long while because a previous venture into the area of faucet repair had turned out badly. But this time I had the manuals from the installation, part numbers, and a good night's sleep. I found the parts in a local plumbing supply house, brought them home and made the installation.

On the human side of my life, I helped my wife overcome a kidney infection. We'd been noticing a change in her behavior starting on Wednesday, lots of sleep and loss of appetite. We exchanged calls with her doctor, and a quick visit to the local ER on Friday afternoon was recommended. It confirmed nasty bugs were in control. IVs were run, drugs pumped, and pills prescribed. By Saturday morning she was back in action. Eating, drinking, and taking daily strolls.

I wish fighting off her dementia was as easy. But all anyone can do is watch. And it's an impossibly long show with no good ending. Still, it feels nice to keep opportunistic predators at bay, because she likes to see me and listen to music and take walks. Parts of what made her the person everyone loved still seem to be there, and that is worth defending, so defend it we shall.

1,2,3

Saturday, November 23, 2019

It was an all-around good day yesterday. Had an early Thanksgiving lunch with my wife and the families of other folks living with her. The day started out overcast and drizzly, but turned clear and cool by midday. There was an abundance of food with tables inside and out. My wife and I chose the latter, to sit in the shelter of the porch with the warming sun on our backs. Although, to be fair, I made the choice and my wife followed because I had the food. When we finished, we cleared our plates and went to sit together in her room until she indicated she wanted to take a nap. I helped her into bed and took my leave.

The afternoon was taken up with band practice. My youngest son has asked me to join a small four piece band they'd put together. I play rhythm guitar. It's fun being part of something larger than yourself, playing a role, taking instruction, learning parts. It makes me wish I'd been in a band in high school; unfortunately, I never attended a high school that had a band until I was midway through my junior year. Oh, well, it's never too late to learn and learning is fun. I enjoy immersing myself in the strictures and structures of music and even though I'm on the long end of the actuarial table, I might as well go out singing and playing guitar.

In the evening, I hooked up with my youngest brother and a friend who'd come in from Houston to go hear music at the dance hall in Albert. My father lived in Albert as a little boy just across the road from the dance hall where we were standing. That was in the 1930s. Here I was, again, nearly ninety years later. As expected, a large group of friends showed up, and we hugged, and drank and danced, and just generally had a good time. When the music ended, we all stood on the dance floor and talked with one another and the members of the band. Then each of us started drifting away, back to our lives, and the dark roads home.

Preparation

Tuesday, November 26, 2019

The leaves on two of our four lacey oaks are now gold or almost gold. Soon, we'll have one last splash of color and then all the leaves will be on the ground. Just in time for Thanksgiving. Winter in the yard may officially start. I was beginning to wonder if I had misremembered their pattern, or that as the trees aged and grew, they had changed their habits. I shall wonder no more.

The outside Christmas lights are up. I am going to replace the icicle lights adorning the house because they've gotten dull with too many missing sections. It looks as though they've been hanging around since last Christmas. It's sort of sad. I think if my wife had been in the game last year she would have remonstrated me and I would have made the change then. It's harder to self-regulate than you imagine. I miss my light-loving partner.

I'm going to try and finish up today. There's a wreath to put on the front gate and garlands to hang around the front door. I have extra lights and I may try to find places for them. The beds around the big oaks need help. The laser lights I got for the trees look fine in small doses but are overwhelmed by our ambient city light on a larger scale. The yard needs more brightness, and it shall have it. This little light of mine, I'm gonna let it shine.

'Tis the Season 3

Friday 3, November 29, 2019

Here we are, the day after Thanksgiving. Yesterday my youngest son and I visited his mother in her quarters. We sat with her, walked with her, took her for a ride, and stopped for a soft drink and a cookie before getting her settled in. Back at home, we wheeled out the big grill, stuffed the firebox with blackjack oak, burned it down to coals, and grilled two steaks I'd picked up at the local butcher the day before. New York strips. Medium rare. I marinated mine, he wanted his plain. We have meat left over. Abundance.

While the fire was burning, I finished lighting up the yard. Changed out the broken dingy lights on the fence and put up the bright, new ones, cool white LEDs. Took down the dead solar lights on the gate and put up warm white electrics that come on with the rest when the sun goes down. I added a spotlight to shine on the big trees. Tonight is the Lights Spectacular in Johnson City when the Courthouse shines, fireworks boom, and the PEC courtyard is turned into a winter wonderland.

Now starts the commercial season of Christmas filled with decorations, shopping, and the anxiety of the perfect gift. There will be parties and dinners. Come Sunday people will light Advent candles. Christmas trees will go up. Angels will appear on mantles. I'll do my part. Decorate. Be festive. Be of good cheer. I'd say it might be hard, but I enjoy Christmas. It lifts my spirits. Sure, there are bad things happening in my life. But even though it would be easy to let the dark overwhelm me, in the light it is possible to see a way forward.

How Does Your Garden Grow

Monday, December 2, 2019

Back in 2010 men with chainsaws worked on my big oaks. Months earlier the oaks had collapsed from the drought and for all intents and purposes looked dead. I thought the men doing the work were arborists. But no. They were merely men with chainsaws. The results made me cry. I called in a true arborist. He told me to turn the ground beneath the trees, loosen the soil, lose the grass. I did all that and then some. Gradually, with time and with water, the trees revived. They even returned, as if spirits, from the earth whence stumps had been ground.

Today, nine years on, the crowns are crowning, branches extending, and the big trees look strong and healthy. Along their base and mingled with their roots are scarlet sage, lantana, and spiderworts. My son has planted little understory trees, Eve's necklace and redbud. It's a community, sharing water, taking nutrients from the earth, giving back. The grass still likes the moist earth, but with my help it's gradually shrinking its footprint. The little interlocked community of plants and trees seems healthy and thriving.

I was reminded of this, as I made my way to musical events with friends and acquaintances this past weekend to see entertainers we know and love. I was in a garden of friendships, a mix of people and personalities, each of us giving and receiving sustenance in the measures required, as we shared handshakes and hugs and raised our voices in song and laughter. The added beauty of it all, and the thing striking hardest, was that, unlike earth-bound gardens, proximity is merely a reminder of our good fortune. Our garden most truly exists in our minds and in our lives. We cultivate it at our leisure. And, most amazingly, it is totally within our power to avoid the men with chainsaws.

Hide and Seek

Tuesday, December 3, 2019

I had a brief I'm-losing-my-mind moment this morning. My house slippers disappeared. Now, if it was a dog or a cat, you might think they'd run off. But being slippers, they pretty much go where I take them, or leave them. In this instance, I'd left them somewhere I couldn't remember. There was consternation, because despite a relatively long search there was nothing to show for it. I checked all the usual places. Under the coffee table. On top of the couch. In the bed. Even the utility room, because on occasion I wear them outside and leave them there because of attached dirt and debris.

Keep in mind, too, that these are robust house slippers, lined Crocs. They've been in my footwear collection for some time and have outlived two pairs of moccasins. I went back to them this year because my most recent pair of moccasins wore out. I thought of my trusty Crocs. I pulled out the liners, washed them, and we were back in business. But back to the search. I'd looked every place twice and finally ended up at the bedroom closet. All the lights were on, and I was doing a slow scan. Then I spotted them, soles up, by my boots. Relief.

When you're the spouse of a partner with brain disease everything related to memory and cognition becomes a sign you've got it as well. Since you see first-hand what losing your mind is all about, losing your own becomes the real deal. Finding those Crocs saved me from the fears that I might have accidentally put them in the trash, which I'd already taken out this morning, or done some equally mindless thing. Nope. My feet are warm, the coffee is hot, and I can pad through the house in silence, safe with my brain and its memories.

Holding On

Wednesday, December 4, 2019

My Walker's Low catmint mostly bit the dust this summer, the victim of no rain and its owner's inattention to watering. It transformed from a sprawling, verdant, lavender-blue ground cover to a sprawling collection of dead wood. I was prepared to replant. Then the rains came, and there, right in the middle, the catmint came back. It had recovered. I still intend to add a plant, because the recovery has taken place downslope of its original location and plants seldom grow uphill, but the original plant is back and that's good.

This growing downhill is a feature of my back porch, pasture-facing garden. It has a slope and the plants want to follow it and go down, lord knows to where. I guess it's just gravity saying, come, follow me. This winter I plan on terracing parts of it, creating a cascade of flat places that will encourage the plants to stay home. I still think they'll reach the edge and want to go down, but I do believe I can make them more content to stay put and prosper in place. It will also help with water retention and I'm sure that will have a positive impact.

I wish life was as easy to manage as my garden. I'd go right into my wife's brain, clean out that bad tau protein, and give everything a good watering. But humans being humans, terraforming them to our likes and purposes is often a futile thing and even the best doctors hit the limits of their skills and say, simply, sorry, there's no more we can do. Plus, they tend to concentrate on the big problems. As I've said before, there's lots of talk about Alzheimer's but not so much on frontotemporal dementia, just as there's lots of literature on growing grass, not so much on growing catmint. So, failing a last-minute call from the cavalry, it's just me and my bride holding on as best we can.

Goings On

Saturday, December 7, 2019

Big day yesterday. We moved[4] my wife to a new memory care facility. The move was made, I suspect, largely because when you're dealing with a progressive disease, improving the surroundings is the only thing one can do that changes anything. At her new abode, accommodations are slightly more commodious than previous. Her room is larger, there's a private bath, and the crew that cooks for the assisted living folks at the front of the community also cook the meals for the memory care people.

I was aided in the move by our country neighbors just down the road toward Blanco. They were our city neighbors at one point. We met them back in 1975 when they lived next door to my mother-in-law. My youngest son pitched in as well, graciously rescheduling his workday to assist his dad who seems to think everyone is retired and totally flexible. They all moved furniture, hung pictures, and made the little room home, while I drove my wife around. Another couple, friends from before we were married, had also volunteered, but illness intervened.

My wife took a good nap after the hullabaloo of the morning move. She ate well, and after dinner we watched a little television and then went around to a big table at the back to work a puzzle. It was a little square with nine colored images and nine corresponding blocks. You had to put a block on its matching picture. I put the square in front of her, handed her a block and pointed at the picture. She looked. Synapses fired, and she put the block on its square. They fired again and she did another until the page was full. It made me happy, but she looked tired. I put her to bed and headed on home.

---

[4] There was no big prep for this move. It just happened. I'd grown dissatisfied with her previous facility, so when a new one opened I went to visit. I liked it. There was nothing life threatening going on at her previous home. But it was old and had the problems that older facilities have.

A Short Good-bye

Monday, December 9, 2019

Lost a friend this past weekend. A new friend. A post-move to the Hill Country friend. One who came to me on the wings of song. He and his wife are members of a musical community to which I belong. As do most males who work in Texas, we had the oil business in common. And, as it turned out, we also worked for the same company at about the same time. He made it a career. I was passing through. It was a nice secondary talking point.

It was the sort of friendship where I stayed at their house on two occasions when musical events or a party suggested it might be the prudent thing to do rather than risk a drive down winding, deer-laden roads in the dark. It was a nice gesture, a kindness. Given, I suspect, to help ease my burdens even while carrying his own. I'm sure he did it for others as well. We tried to give back. In the dying of the light, we held a private house party for him with the anchor point of our musical community performing. On a second occasion, we simply had a party with friends who brought guitars and sang. He complimented my singing; I have the words hanging in my heart.

I wish I had more stories. He golfed. I love the sport, but we only had a solitary chance to play together. It was always music where our paths crossed, but that's a nice place to get to know someone. His bright smile and joy made it even easier. I wish there was something I could do for his wife and children to ease the burden of his passing. But we all know how that goes. Grief is a solitary burden that can be understood but never lightened. There are prayers, of course, and they shall be offered. It does help to know people are thinking of you, and think of them I shall. Because he was a lovely man, and will be sorely missed.

'Tis the Season 4

Wednesday, December 11, 2019

Baby, it's cold outside. 31 degrees. A light freeze. The cats are up, however. I put out the food, and there they came. I walked over in the dark to turn off the well and drain the tank. The task was probably not required, but I felt better having done it. On the grass in the dark, as I walked to the well, I could see crystals of frost. The waxing gibbous moon shone through the neighbor's trees. It will be full tomorrow.

I got nearly nine hours of sleep last night. The old body gave out about 8:30 p.m. and rose from its slumber at 5:30 a.m. That feels good. I guess the anxiety of moving my wife to a new facility has abated. She seems well adjusted. The staff has the measure of her moods and schedule, the food is plentiful and well-balanced, and the room is clean and well-lighted. Other than having her home and healthy, I'm not sure what more could be asked. The daughter came up Monday and gave her imprimatur as well. We all seem to be good.

The first of the Christmas cards started arriving, which only serves to remind me, I am a bit late in getting mine out. But they are coming or going rather. I bought them right before Thanksgiving, then got caught in the push to move my wife. At least that bit is done. All that is now required is time at the table to write and address. Luckily, I've learned you can do them in bits and pieces, which seems as though it should be intuitively understood. But previously, I tended to think of it as a project that should be done in one sitting as though the cards would spoil if I failed to send them out all at once. That's crazy. I know. I'm over it now. And it didn't take a lot of convincing.

Good Times

Thursday, December 12, 2019

Big moon. The pasture is bathed in white, frost and moonlight. Off in the distance, I can see the dark shape of a deer grazing by the water tank. The southwest breeze is stirring the chill night air, but I suspect we'll be warmer today. I could safely turn the well back on, but there's really no need. Although, the water feature beneath the big oaks needs refreshing, partly because that's where the cats drink. I've talked myself into it. I just need to remember it's on when the hard freezes come.

It's nice how we're slipping into winter, and I can hardly wait for January and February. But we'll hit the solstice in a couple of weeks and turn our eyes to longer days. It's an odd twist. The days will lengthen yet grow colder. At some point we'll hear the words *polar vortex*. Then we'll all duck and run. I'd like to see some snow. We've had several instances since moving to the Hill Country. I'd like another. Just for old time's sake.

The most fun I've had with snow was in 2004. We had the kids over on Christmas Eve. As they pulled out to go home, the snow started. By morning the ground was covered, and our Christmas was white. It was a good day. My wife and I opened our presents, enjoyed the view, sat by the roaring fire, and enjoyed life. Simple pleasures.

Odds and Ends

Tuesday, December 17, 2019

I did it. Christmas cards are out. It was hard this year. Unsure as to the reason. I'd bought them well in advance, but never could make the time to do them. I guess it's a lot of handwriting, and in this day and age, that's a little off-putting. I did short circuit things a bit by using address labels for the return address. It's barely noticeable on the white envelopes, but sticks out like a sore thumb on the red. I hope I'm forgiven.

This is my fourth year at the task. I used the address book my wife had kept up-to-date and noted the year for each family who received a card. The first in the list for most of them is 2010, which was the year after we made the move to Johnson City. I wish I could find the address book she used prior to that. Although, I suspect she already was beginning to distrust her memory and went to logging dates so she could keep up and that there is no other address book.

Later this week I'll begin bringing down bits and pieces of the interior Christmas decorations. We have a white porcelain Santa and Sled that's a favorite. It goes on top of the entertainment center. Then there's the angel collection. My daughter helped me organize and box that last year. Also, we have the lovely nativity scene my wife did during one of her ceramic phases, hand-painted and fired, large Duck included. I rebuilt the manger last year. There are other odds and ends, and I imagine I'll put them up. It's a little hard, but no sense running from the memories. I might as well embrace them. It's a good way to wear down the sharp edges.

Close Call

Wednesday, December 18, 2019

Catastrophe averted. In a casual conversation yesterday morning, my brother mentioned a hard freeze was coming that night. I thought of the things I would need to do, and then promptly forgot them in the welter of doctor appointments, trips to fill prescriptions, and lunch with my wife and some friends who came to see her. The cold weather chores popped back up on my radar at 11:30 p.m. as I readied for bed. My weather station said it was 27 degrees. That, my friends, is a freeze getting hard. My heart-rate ticked up.

I grabbed a flashlight, put on my slippers and went to check the well. I turned it off and tried to open the ball valve to drain the lines. No go. Frozen. Back inside. Filled a pot with hot water. Back outside. Dumped it on the ball valve. Success. The line flushed and ultimately the stream of water went limp and then stopped. Lucky me. There will be no need for a spring repair of the water lines. It was too close for comfort. I really need to get oriented to what's happening in the real world. I guess.

In my youth, I prided myself on preparation skills. I watched the winter weather. Drained lines. Covered faucets. Let things drip all night. Brought in plants. Was Johnny-on-the-spot. Now? My faucets are wrapped with old towels versus fancy Styrofoam covers. My attic water lines are expandable and designed for freezes. And all the plants are native and built for the weather. Except the rose and it's so well sheltered and so old, it fears no one. I am a stranger in a strange land, or at least it feels that way. I drift from dawn till dark with no one to impress or protect, except the cats, reluctant beneficiaries of my food and shelter, and yet they still run when I bend down to pet them.

A Nod to Benoit

Friday, January 3, 2020

On New Year's Day I drove from Fredericksburg to Gruene Hall in New Braunfels. The trip took me past Luckenbach and down into the valley of the Blanco River. The day was gray to start, and as I approached the river, I encountered a heavy fog. In the dark, it would have meant low beams and slow driving. The last remnants of daylight, however, meant I was simply entombed in a veil of gray, focused solely on my strip of asphalt.

As I drove, I wondered if this was to be the state of my journey. I thought, if it were, I was in for a long trip and perhaps I'd be better served heading home. Fortunately, the answer was no. As I reached the town of Blanco and moved off toward Fischer, the fog lifted, along with my spirits. I had a clear road. The skies were still gray, but I could see. If not forever, at least enough to feel less confined. The remainder of the trip was easy and came to a stop in a parking space only a few short feet from the door of my destination. It seemed a good sign, because normally parking on this day was at a premium.

Inside the Hall, music was thumping, and crowds of people were milling about and standing to watch the band. At first they were all strangers, and then I began to see faces I knew. A fair number of them were standing on the benches that line the Hall's north wall. As their smiles and greetings rained down on me and I met the warm embrace of others standing in front of them, I felt good. And in that moment, I could see that the pattern of the afternoon was the pattern of my day, my week, my month, my year. A fractal full of fog, doubt, clarity, music, love, all swirling in the small and larger eddies of a life being lived.

A Christmas Tale

Saturday, January 4, 2020

This is the story of a gift. A bar of soap. Handmade. Scented with sandalwood. Given at Christmas. I liked it. Took it home. Bathed with it. Felt refreshed. Tried to buy more. Visited the company website. Found no soap. Queried the giver of the gift. Thought perhaps it was obtained from a store. I needed the name. I really wanted more of this soap. Then the gift giver confessed. It came to her as a gift. She had no idea as to its origin.

At this point, I suppose I could have been disappointed at being re-gifted, but there was more to the story. The gift giver knew I liked sandalwood. She held onto the soap and kept it, just for me. It was a nice gesture. And I do like sandalwood. I still have a bottle of sandalwood cologne bought at a Crabtree and Evelyn store just off Covent Garden in London. God only knows how old it is. It all started when my wife brought home bars of scented soap from a Fiesta supermarket in Houston. It became my soap of choice, faithfully replenished by my wife during her grocery shopping forays for 40-plus years.

I had no idea my daughter knew this. It seemed a small, behind the scenes thing. Invisible. I guess that's why she's a good teacher. She pays attention. Like mother, like daughter. Her mother knew people's names. She knew the names of their children. She knew their ages. She knew birthdays. She knew fun things about them. She knew little things about people that allowed for the giving of small personal gifts. And that's why I really like this particular bar of soap. It feels like a gift from my wife given through a chosen intermediary.

And, Now This

Tuesday, January 7, 2020

Yesterday, as I was exploring here and there, war and peace, hungry and full, and began thinking about a range of states that were one thing then another, and talked about the and, the space between them, the journey, I ran across lonely. I wrote sad and happy, lonely and …. I had to stop. What's the opposite of lonely? In the journey of moving from one state to another, where are you going if you're leaving lonely?

I suspect most of us hardly ever think about it. If we feel lonely, or what passes for lonely, we pick up the phone and call someone. It's a sort of transitory state with an easy solution, and barely registers. But what about someone who is lonely to the point it affects their health, and studies show it does, and it's a killer. That kind of lonely. A locked in lonely. A steady state. The lack of a defined opposite might mean it's really difficult to get away, because the solution is described as a negative. How to not be lonely. You're running from something rather than to something. I imagine it can start to feel hopeless.

I did read one article, in which the author chronicled the positive effects of simply talking to chronic visitors to the ER. She reached out, talked to them, visits decreased. She posited they wanted to feel connected, and maybe that's the opposite, connected. And connections are something under our control. Although, and this may be key, a connection is a two-way street, as in, it takes two to tango. The lesson? Get those receptors out because you might be helping someone escape the curse of loneliness.

Part of a Day

Thursday, January 9, 2020

Went for a walk yesterday. It covered a little over 2.5 miles. It was interspersed with riding, bending, swinging. It was enough exercise that I'm sore this morning, and my right hip feels a little achy. It was a windy walk and a little on the chilly side, but the wind was the big news. It blew hard, and I don't know why but it had a tiring effect. Maybe my body was resisting the wind, bending into the force. On the other hand, lately I have noticed, more often than not, my rounds of golf leave me a little piqued. I guess it's just that old age thing.

On the way home I stopped in to have dinner with my wife. She was sleeping when I got there but roused herself fairly fast and we made our way into the dining room. She ate as I talked, uncomprehending, and told her about my day. When she finished, we took a walk and then sat by the fireplace in the lobby. Eventually, we made our way to the long craft table and worked a couple of puzzles. I take them apart for her and lay out the pieces much as she would have done. She knows just what to do, taking each piece and fitting it to its spot, always starting with a corner. She still has an eye for how the pieces fit together. It's amazing to watch her turn the piece until it's just right, and then push it into place. Her eyes move over the board and when she encounters a piece that's slightly out of place, she slows. Her hands turn it as she searches for its home, comparing colors and edges and shapes. It reminds me of the days when she worked 1,500-piece puzzles. Of course, these days the puzzles have 25 pieces and are intended for a three-year-old, but I don't think she cares.

I took it slow on the drive home, because I've seen lots of deer on the road lately, between Fredericksburg and Johnson City, both dead and alive, and I have no desire to beat up my car or bring about the demise of one of them. Mostly, it's 55 at night, all the way home, which means I don't need to slow down in Hye or Stonewall. Can't say I notice much difference in the time the trip takes, either. I guess when we get back to the summer sun, I'll probably speed up, but for now, I'm good with slow and steady, and trust me when I tell you, I'm not racing anyone.

Last Night

Saturday, January 11, 2020

Our house is built along an east-west axis with eight-foot porches. This means I can stand on the southern porch when a norther blows through and stay dry and out of the wind. That's what I did last night when the big storm came. My son was there, too. He's built a nice masonry storm drain out of native rocks at the southwest corner, and this was really his first chance to see it perform. It was magic. He saw some shortcomings, but that's the way of all artists.

It was nice to have a big rain. We got nearly an inch. We could use more, but I'll take what we got. The north wind is still filling in behind the storm, bringing cold air. Just a taste of winter, however, nothing too hard. Overall, we've had a soft winter and dry, too. Nothing like last year when it seemed to rain constantly. But, that's the Hill Country, sitting smack on top of the 98th meridian, which will soon be the new dividing line between the wet east and the dry west. I imagine we'll be trending a bit drier than the old days unless something changes in the global climate.

The only comfort I have is that the change will be slow, and most folks won't notice or much care because humans being humans, they think their biological clock is the clock by which all else is measured. They fail to understand that we're right up there with the fruit fly compared to the geological clock, which is ticking inexorably toward making us all part of the fossil record.

Lah Di Dah

Monday, January 13, 2020

I try to be tidy, but I'm not tidy like my wife is tidy. Even with dementia, she beats me all to pieces. She's still shutting doors, straightening silverware, and folding napkins even as she taste-tests a piece of cotton because it looks like food. The tidy tendency must be hardwired in the same place that holds all her music memories. Some people say dementia will reveal a person's true character and, judging by my wife, that's true. She's a tidy, sweet, music loving lady.

We had a nice visit yesterday. We worked a bunch of puzzles and ate lunch. We have to grind her food now, because her chewing has become disassociated from her swallowing. The soft food goes down in a more or less normal fashion. The staff had her washing all done, so I folded up the clothes that needed folding and hung the rest in her closet. I know they're paid to do it, but it makes me feel useful and it maybe gave them time with another resident who needed it more.

I left her watching TV and slipped away to join-in at a picker's circle with some old friends and some new friends. That was a nice way to close out the afternoon. We even had chili and tamales and homemade sweets. I snuck a taste of the host's honey flavored whiskey, too. He saw me do it; in fact he poured me the first shot. It was probably a mistake because I promptly forgot the second verse of "Tennessee Whiskey" and it only has two verses. Oh, well, that's the nice thing about picker's circles. We're all there to have fun and encourage one another and no one is going to hold a dropped lyric against you. Besides, as one of my professional friends says, it's a free show.

Thoughts on the Cube Farm

Wednesday, January 15, 2020

Hey, Hey. Another solid night of sleep. More dreams. Fuzzy on the details, but the overall thrust was plain. It was cube life, as in work, and the right-before-waking-up part of the dream had a co-worker getting new glasses, which is exactly what I did yesterday, and we were all sharing our new glasses stories. Or, maybe I was getting ready to share my new glasses story and woke up because that was reality, and my brain wanted me awake so I could get going. I do not know.

Anyway, I got new glasses yesterday. I got the prescription back in July, put it on the freezer in the utility room with a magnet, and waited for an opportunity to fill it. This makes it sound as though I was waiting for the exact right alignment of the sun, moon, and stars, but the case is more mundane. I just didn't want to take the time or spend the money. Last week the spirit moved me, and I did the deed. Don't be looking for a new stylistic me, however; I bought exactly the same frame style as my old glasses, which is why I still wear khaki slacks and blue jeans. It's just easier.

But back to cube life. I lived the first two-thirds of my post-college working life in offices, as in a private space with a door. The cube farm came in the latter years, and I found it moderately appealing. There was a nice sense of community and that was part of the revelation I had this morning. Today, a typical day of retirement, I will speak to one other person, maybe two, face to face. At work, I would have seen a multitude and spoken to at least half of them. That's a lot of interaction. Perhaps this is why some people find retirement to be less than expected. Loss of human contact. And maybe that's why I write, because anyone reading this is another person poking their head over the cube wall, and saying good morning.

Small Town Life

Friday, January 17, 2020

Yeah. It rained all day yesterday. At least it seemed so. Let's just say it there was a high probability of getting wet if you went outside, and I went outside a lot yesterday. I ran errands all over town. Went to the newly opened branch of a bank with which I do business. They were still checking out their computer systems, but they let me in. I made the payment and got my picture taken with the president, as the branch's first customer. I may have to do more business with such nice people.

Later in the day, I got my car inspected. It was raining, as I mentioned, and that used to put a damper on inspections, but things have changed as they tend to do, and we got it done. I then renewed my tags.

You can do that online, which might be a real timesaver if I lived in Harris County, but given that I live in a sparsely populated rural county it gives me a chance to get out and about. That evening I made the trip west to have dinner with my wife, and then went shopping for some vittles. Saw a friend, got a hug, exchanged pleasantries, and made my way home in the dark.

The heifers and their calves spent most of the day up close to the house by the fence. The little ones, as usual, spooked when I came out on the porch. One, however, held his ground and continued to sniff the air. I wasn't sure what such boldness would get him, but it was striking. They're still eating the cactus, spines and all, which I find unusual. Eventually, the little ones will gain some weight and size and head off to market where they will find other pastures, maybe greener than mine, and there will be just the heifers and a bull to start the process all over again. And it's supposed to rain again today.

Helping

Monday, January 20, 2020

M ost of my visits with my wife come at mealtime. The tables are arranged restaurant style, four chairs to a table. The meals come up from the kitchen and are served by the caregivers. We generally get a table to ourselves. Her meals are ground now because of her swallowing difficulties, but she hardly notices. She still likes portions separated from one another and she'll eat all of one before tackling the next. We've all noticed she eats the ground meals with a slower, more measured pace. We've surmised that with chewing out of the equation the swallow reflex is more easily triggered.

My roles are to keep her water glass full, because that helps with her swallowing, and to ensure that she doesn't over-fill her mouth, which still happens on occasion. I had never really thought about how much brain power is expended in the act of eating until I watched my wife lose control over a function that all of us take totally for granted. Put food in your mouth, chew, swallow, take the next bite. She takes bites and chews and forgets to swallow. Not a good thing to forget. Fortunately, there is now a team of people watching to help her remember.

When I'm there, I like to feed her the dessert. She offers no objection. I spoon out a little bite, offer it to her, and she takes it. I watch to ensure she's chewed and swallowed before proffering the next bit. She watches back. It's the same motion and ritual I used while raising three children. Maybe it's that connection that makes it so fulfilling, despite the ominous nature of what it really means, a false hope that saves us from the despair of reality. If that's the case, delude me. I'm good with it.

Music, Beer, and Friends

Friday, January 24, 2020

It's amazing how the familiarity of a drive can make it seem easy and quick. When we first moved to the Hill Country, driving to Gruene in New Braunfels for a show was almost a deal breaker. It took GPS and planning to mount a campaign. Now, several years in, and free of the GPS tyrant, a drive to Gruene is a trip down familiar roads. I know where to find parking, how to grab a bite before the show, and how to dress for the weather. Which is why yesterday, when I realized a friend had a band gig there last night, I mounted up and did the spur-of-the-moment thing.

It was a providential move. I had a nice meal. Friends and family were there, some that I don't see at all the shows. The band was in fine form, and I managed to survive four hours on the music hall's rock-hard benches because of it. Most of us tarried after the show to talk to the musicians, which is a big part of the fun of going to shows, and then we made our ways to our respective homes. It was a good evening, and the music and the friendship went a long way to filling some of life's little voids.

Today, I'll have lunch with my bride, and then in the afternoon, I'll make another journey to a friend's ranch to spend a couple of days in the country. I'll tell my wife all about it, but I might as well be speaking ancient Greek. These days, it's the ceremony that counts. She still knows I'm telling her stuff, and I think she still appreciates the visits, but I suspect we may be moving close to the point [5]where that tenuous connection of memory may be about to break. That will be a hard day. I think I'll just ignore it.

---

[5] There's no hard data to support this, just a feeling from watching these past several years as things progressively worsen. You're always on the lookout, sensitive to even the smallest change.

Weekend News

Monday, January 27, 2020

Spent the weekend in the country. There were two couples and me. A little unbalanced, but we survived. We talked about gophers, wild hogs, and good neighbors. We drank whiskey, ate fine food, and sang songs. We sat around the fire for a bit, but it started to rain. We toured the house, toured the ranch, and walked in the woods. We even made a visit to the closest town for lunch and a little shopping. It was an easy drive there and an easy drive back. I'd mark it as a pleasurable success.

After my return to home, I fired up the mower and trimmed the winter grass. The ranch's trim pastures made me feel like a laggard. I avoided our nascent group of bluebonnets, because we'll need them this spring. Today, I'll edge around the gardens. The weather is cool and conducive to outdoor work. I shall do some. Probably more than some, but it's supposed to rain tomorrow, or is it tonight? I could look, but recently, I've found myself slightly less addicted to knowing what was happening or going to happen every minute of the day. I've gotten to the point of waking up, looking outside, and making my decision on the fly.

On a side note, I've stopped using cream in my coffee, partly because I ran out and figured it was something I didn't need to buy. Also, I wondered how it would go down if I just brewed it, popped in a little honey, and started drinking. So far, so good. This is the second thing I've given up because I was too lazy to go to the store; the other thing was ice. My wife always insisted on having a freezer full. We'd get a 20-lb. bag and dump it in. Nowadays I only get ice when company comes, and for the rest of the time you can make it yourself. That's good to know when it comes to spending money.

Up and At 'em

Wednesday, January 29, 2020

Had a busy day yesterday. It included a business lunch, a planning and zoning meeting, and a candidate forum. At the end, when I arrived home, I stood in the dark of my yard and looked up at the waxing crescent moon. It hung clear and bright in the rain-washed sky. Just below, Venus put on a sparkly show. I felt oddly at peace with the flow of my life for the first time in a good while. Not sure what that means, really. Perhaps getting regular amounts of sleep works as advertised.

I do know that once I was in the house, I ate a slightly late dinner and read a little bit. Strangely enough, I had no desire to turn on the television. The quiet reverie of the moon-watch was a better end-of-day visual. I closed out the evening with a cup of warm milk and honey. I'm pretty sure this beverage isn't what Moses had in mind when he set off to trek around in the desert for forty years. I have no idea why I decided to try it last year, but I did, and it's a really nice end-of-evening drink, nonetheless.

This morning there's a lovely orange tint in the eastern sky, and the air is still and chill. Bodes well for the day ahead. Of course, there remains the issue of my wife in memory care, but it is what it is, and all anyone can do is deal with it. She's well taken care of and that does give me peace, such as it is. At this stage of my life, that's a pretty good deal, and I'm going to run with it. No sense wasting the day worrying about what could have been.

Rising in the Dark

Thursday, January 30, 2020

I like walking around in the dark, particularly the early morning dark. Things are just starting to wake up and the world feels full of potential. Just now I watched headlights drive up the park road behind the house. Very mysterious, especially when the only thing you're used to seeing is the occasional deer. It was a truck of some sort, most likely park rangers getting ready to go about their day. I hope it's going to be a good one for them.

My calendar, by comparison, is empty, although I have things I want to do. I wonder if I should start putting them on the calendar. At the moment, I mainly keep a mental checklist, which is insanely easy to shuffle and gets shuffled a lot. For instance, I had three folding chairs lying in the garage for the better part of–I don't really even know. If my wife had been at hand, they wouldn't have been there a day. I put them up yesterday because I felt good and the clutter was starting to wear on me.

Sometimes I miss the days of the full calendar with meetings and calls and deadlines, but most days no. I still rise at a set time, and try to have things planned out, but I like being able to spend an hour talking to my son about my granddaughter's track team, or my daughter about her school day, without feeling as though I have to cut things short for a meeting or a task. After all, there's no guarantee that the time we've allotted on our calendar for work will be there later for us to spend with family. I think that has something to do with the grand scheme of things and knowing that that piece of clutter will be there tomorrow for me to pick up.

196

Looking Inside

Friday. January 31, 2020

I took down the bedroom TV. It hung over my closet on the opposite side of the room from our bed. It was there because my wife liked it, and usually went to bed with the TV on. I think it was a habit of youth when it was pretty much her only companion after her mother divorced and remarried. I, on the other hand never had a TV in my room, and never much watched it because my mother was a strict TV monitor. I was familiar with Lawrence Welk and Gunsmoke, but not the Untouchables; too violent.

Anyway, in the world of marriage, compromises are inevitable, and I compromised. It's the sort of thing that ties a couple together and makes them "us" rather than "you and me." It's also what makes the undoing of a marriage, either by death or divorce, so hard. "Us" is a lot more than merely the sum of its parts. It's a whole other being, the couple, their kids, their family. Taking it apart is the emotional equivalent of doing surgery on Siamese Twins. There's lots of shared stuff and it hurts when you tug at it and it happens in real time, and there's no anesthesia.

I suspect that's what I've been going through these last several years as my wife's dementia has broken some of the bonds that created "us." I had to rediscover me, and I wasn't really prepared for that, and had no desire to do it. I was happy with "us" and I was trying hard to make the broken bits work. At this point, however, I've come closer to acknowledging the inevitable. And while that is certainly painful, at least I can take solace in knowing that a large part of "us" still remains, and that the new me won't resemble the old me by any stretch of the imagination. All thanks to a wife with whom I compromised.

197

Epilogue

When the book went into production, my wife was still alive, and I was counting on more time. Unfortunately, that's no longer the case. Pharaby Ann Wilson died August 4, 2020. She will be missed.

Acknowledgements

The first acknowledgement any writer makes should be to his editor, the eagle eye who reads every word, helps put structure to them when needed, and discards the redundant and useless. If you have doubts as to the benefits of an editor check the facsimile edition of The Wasteland and see how Ezra Pound helped T.S. Elliot. Or look into Maxwell Perkins and Ernest Hemingway and F. Scott Fitzgerald. I'm not in the class of any of those writers, to be sure, but I rely on my editor in much the same fashion as they did. Which is why I acknowledge the work of Peggy Stautberg, a soft-spoken, hard-working genius.

In the category of people who did things to make the book better is my daughter, Brianne Morse, who designed our new logo, Julie Sckittone who designed the covers, and Jerry Chrisman who was responsible for the interior design and overall production assistance. Jerry has held my hand through a lot of similar projects over the course of the last twenty-years and I've run out of ways to thank him.

Next up, one should acknowledge his supporters, especially, the ones who pumped the ego and said, go ahead, you're good, with nothing to gain by offering their support. Chief among these, at this stage of my writing career, is Walt Wilkins, a songwriter and performer of note, whose off-handed compliment one day made my heart sing and made me feel it was okay to keep going. His wife, Tina, was also there offering words of kind support. And following close in line are two other songwriters of skill and reputation, Davis Raines, and Jimmy Davis.

Oddly enough, I also have fans in amongst my group of friends. Jerry and Martha Jones, Nancy Laura, Nancy Rodenbusch, Kris and Gary Wallis, Tim and Kim Melgaard, Mike Malone, Anne Hayden, Tempe Williams-Thomas, Marilynn Turnbull, Dorothy Lurie,

Melinda Anne Lowery and Phil Hook, Tressie and James Sharkey, and Tracy Carroll. They're all good people who've managed to pass along a compliment or two over the years. To them, and those I've missed, I say thank you with gratitude.

About the Author

John W. Wilson has written for the Houston Chronicle, Houston City Magazine, Texas Sports, The Christian Science Monitor, and Omni. He also has served as the director of the Book Division at Gulf Publishing Company in Houston.

He's won awards for his fiction and poetry, including the collegiate division of The Atlantic Monthly. He also has received numerous awards during his decades-long career in industrial communication.

In 2000, John and his wife, Pharaby, founded J. Wilson and Associates, Inc., which specializes in technical editing, data management, and process management. The company also has published books and distributed titles for a variety of publishers.

Made in the USA
Coppell, TX
02 November 2020

40656483R00118